Mission: Open Heavens – Module 1

AWAKENING THE CHURCH

John Mulinde & Mark Daniel

A Publication of WTMA
Orlando, FL

Published by World Trumpet Mission

First printing 2010

ISBN 978-0-615-40764-7

To order additional copies of this workbook, write to World Trumpet Mission, PO Box 770447, Orlando, FL 32877; email media@worldtrumpet.com; phone (407)846-8300; or order online at www.worldtrumpet.com.

Printed in the United States of America

World Trumpet Mission
PO Box 770447
Orlando, FL 32877
www.worldtrumpet.com

Mission: Open Heavens – Module 1

AWAKENING THE CHURCH

Table of Contents

Acknowledgment

We would like to thank the many people who helped develop this workbook and make it a reality.

- We would first like to thank the Ugandan missionaries who have given themselves so sacrificially over the years. May the price you have paid to see the nations transformed bring you much heavenly reward.

- Thanks also go to those around the world who have welcomed WTM and allowed the message to pierce their hearts and rise up to see God move in their land. May the Lord continue to give you a deep hunger to see transforming revival in your nation.

- We would like to thank June Perez, who spent months bringing together and editing these teachings, going through the process of laying out the text, and managing all aspects of the production of this workbook. We also thank Clare Hamilton, who was a great support with June, helping to write, edit, research, and gather information as needed. Without them, this work would not be in written form.

- We also want to thank those who helped transcribe, write, edit, proofread, research, and design every page of this workbook: Rick Borage, Kath Brown, Gardner Daniel, Pam Davidson, Cliff Lara, Rebecca Lara, Bill McCann, Jonathan McGill, Jim Mozdren, Joyce Nantongo, Maelynn Perez, Kelly Sorensen, Mary Sparks, Chris Vennetti, and Jessica Wagner.

- Finally, many people around the world supported this effort with their prayers, for which we are particularly grateful.

Preface

This workbook was born out of a season of examining the fruitfulness of our ministry. World Trumpet Mission had been working for over 20 years in cities and nations around the world, but we weren't seeing the long-term changes that our hearts yearned for. We were "blowing the trumpet" and calling the church to awaken, seeing people and churches being affected and revived wherever we would go, but God had put it in our hearts that we would see something more. God had given us the vision of an army rising and of Him moving in a way that would transform the nations; He had put it in our hearts to see a mighty move of His hand. We desired to see this all this come about, so we began to seek Him for the fruit that only He can bring.

As we measured the impact and fruitfulness of our work, we discovered that although it was undeniable that we had made tremendous impact on many cities and nations over the years, and had even changed the course of some of those nations, the retention levels of the ground we had taken were low! In many instances, after a few years, the fruit of the work had backslidden into old ways. Given that the Master requires of us to "bear much fruit, and that our fruit should remain," we were forced to seriously ask what needed to change.

As we began our quest to find out what we needed to do as individuals and as a ministry to become more fruitful for the Lord in all tangible and measurable ways, and to see our fruits abide, the Holy Spirit began to quicken us to a number of things. The scripture that became the foundation of our search was John 6:28: "*What must we do to do the works God requires?*"

As we prayed into this verse, the Holy Spirit revealed to us several things that are crucial in fulfilling our calling and in bearing much fruit for the Lord. The first is that not every church activity or good act that we do is necessarily the work God is requiring from us. We learned that ministry is fulfilling the heart desires of God, nothing more and nothing less! We also learned that when we come to understand the process by which God works, we can see what His intentions are and what exactly He wants to accomplish in a specific situation. This is critical in revealing to us the bigger vision and mission that God has; seeing His work alone is not sufficient. Once we understand God's intentions and mission, we are able to then see His goals and desired objectives, which enables us to join Him in His work. It also enables us to measure our fruitfulness; if we are meeting His goals and objectives, then we are doing ministry—fulfilling the desires of God's heart. If we are not meeting these goals, then we know to cry out and ask Him to restore us to the commission that He has assigned to us.

By God's grace, we began to see why our ministry was not bearing long-lasting fruit. We could recognize those areas where we were not fulfilling God's heart desires. And because we want to fulfill the destiny for which we were created and fill the desires of God's heart, we were grateful to have been bestowed with this understanding, which we endeavor to share with you in this workbook. We pray that the Lord will enable us to walk this out, as we also pray for you.

This is not a light course. It is likely to be more intense and require more of you than most studies you have done in the past. Every piece of the study—every audio message, all the readings and times of prayer, all the exercises and times of reflection—are to help you be able to rise up and function at a level that can break through, that can bear long-lasting fruit.

We are going to spend these next 2 months plowing more deeply into God's mission, the state of the nations, the state of the church, the challenges that the church is facing, and what God is calling us to do to fulfill His mission in our day and time. As you go through this study, continue to encourage yourself that this plowing is fruitful, that it is helping us to go deeper, bringing us to a place in the Spirit and in our own hearts that God will be able to use to advance His kingdom, and that He is preparing vessels He can use to accomplish His work. Pray that these lessons will begin to take hold of us and begin to stir deeply within us so that we can rise up, ready to go forth as part of God's army to really begin to bring change to the nations. Pray that the Lord will open our hearts and minds as we begin to seek answers to the question, *"What must we do to do the works that God requires?"*

John Mulinde
Kampala, Uganda
October 2010

How to Use This Study

This study is intensive, but is aimed to help us rise up and function at a level where we can break through. The course will require a great deal of you; it is important at the outset that you understand the time that will be required and that you give yourself to it. The more you engage in this study, the audio messages, the reading, and the prayer times, the greater the benefit and the deeper the message can be established in you.

How Is the Study Arranged?

- This workbook study is arranged in seven weekly sections, with four lessons to complete each week. Each week of study includes an audio teaching and four written lessons, for five days of study. Students are requested to do this study in a small group setting, so there will also be one meeting a week with the small group to share what the Holy Spirit is revealing. The group time will also be a means to encourage and strengthen one another as the study progresses.
- There is an audio teaching to listen to before beginning each week's study; the links to these teachings are found on the introduction pages of the weekly studies. Begin each week by listening to the corresponding message; allow it to sink into and plough up the ground of your heart in preparation for the lessons of that week.
- There are weekly and daily prayer targets, which are a central and vital part of this study. These are to be part of your daily prayer time as you go through each week's lessons. The teachings help to lead us in the right direction, but it is only as we are before the Lord in prayer that we will see the breakthroughs begin to come.
- The lessons are comprised of teachings, exercises, times for reflection, times for prayer, and times for responses to each day's lesson. Please try to do as much of the study as possible to get the greatest benefit.

Can I Do This Study Alone or Is It Necessary to be in a Group?

Working through this study with a group—with the framework of fellowship, prayer support, and discussion around the subjects being considered—will be of far greater benefit than doing it alone. While each lesson is designed to be worked through individually, the intention is that a small group of people who are each working through the book would come together once a week to discuss elements of what is being taught and what the Holy Spirit is revealing.

The ground we are seeking to gain will involve spiritual warfare. If you do not have others around you, it will be difficult to persevere and gain the full ground that you are seeking. You really do need the support and encouragement that comes with walking with others.

How Much Time Does the Study Require?

We expect that each week you will spend 8 to 10 hours working through this study, 1 to 2 hours listening to the teaching at the beginning of the week and then approximately 1 to 2 hours per day for each lesson, including the prayer time. Please make a commitment in your heart right now to give the time needed to complete each day's lessons; otherwise, it is easy to lay the workbook aside and not stay caught up with the lessons.

What Will I Need?

Apart from the time committed to work through the study, to pray, and to meet with your group, you will need the determination to persevere, as well as a Bible and a writing utensil.

What Are Prayer Targets?

Every day's lessons includes "prayer points," which are meant to serve as a help for direction in prayer. The Holy Spirit is the One who knows what we ought to pray – not us – but as we come purposing to pray into something, as we give ourselves to a "target," we always see more of the desired result in prayer.

The prayer targets should give you things to "walk out." There is a spiritual position that we're fighting for, a spiritual reality that we're seeking to come into, and as we begin to gain the ground in the spiritual realm we will begin to impact the physical realm. Therefore, the prayer targets are essential, because you will be seeking to gain ground in the spiritual realm, which will begin to give you authority, insight, and understanding to be able to impact the physical realm. Much of the message will be to provoke you in spirit so that you will go before the Lord and begin to gain spiritual ground in your life and in what God has given you influence over.

What Does It Mean to "Pray Into" a Position?

When God has revealed that there is something more He wants to lead us into, we must give ourselves to "praying (ourselves) into" that position. We see that God is calling us to a higher place, a deeper place, a new place, and that we are not yet "there." Because we have never been here before (Joshua 3:4) we must follow the Spirit in all ways. As we are seeking to gain new ground we must hold up the things that God has said. We hold up who He is and what He has done. We proclaim His faithfulness for all that He *has* done—and we pray into believing that He *will do* what we know He is saying that He will do.

As you are praying into this position, the Lord can speak new things to you that He wants you to do (eg, give something up; obey a certain command; humble yourself in a specific situation). In addition, the Holy Spirit brings to remembrance the things that have already been spoken as a reminder/conviction to walk in the way you have been told.

Bless You as You Complete This Study

May the Lord carry your through this study, and may He write deeply on your heart all that is required for Him to use you to fulfil His purposes in our day. May He uphold you and strengthen you as you begin this quest to learn, *What must we do to do the works that God requires?*

Week 1.

A Wake-Up Call

GOAL OF THE WEEK:

This week we want to
1. Begin to look at the state of the world and the response of the church, and how we can begin to have real impact in the nations
2. Come to a place of desperation for God and seeing His purposes fulfilled in the nations

As we travel the nations, we have met a lot of people using a phrase I had not heard before: "revival fatigue." People are trying to do everything they can to see God move mightily in their cities and nations, and yet many of them are not seeing anything happen. There are people laboring to bring unity, laboring to raise up prayer, laboring to bring compassion ministries into their cities, but they are not experiencing the breakthroughs they are looking for, and their work and ministry are not withstanding the warfare that is coming against them. They begin to lose the courage to seek, they begin to lose the passion to keep going, and they begin to feel like it is futile and is not going to have any impact. They lose their hope and they begin to experience this "revival fatigue."

I believe we can and are called to have impact in our cities and nations, but what we have been seeing is man trying to do God's work in human ways and on human terms, and God is not responding to that. This led us to develop a study such as the one you are about to begin. In this study, we will ask many important questions: How can we begin to see the works of God? How do we do the work of God so that it brings impact, change, and transformation? How is the church going to truly present Christ as the hope to the nations?

The scriptures give us a great deal of insight into God's work and His perspective. To understand what is involved in the true work of God, we must go back to the scriptures. For example, we need to find those things that God said would open the heavens and we must devote ourselves to them. There are spiritual principles that are essential to understand and apply. If we just focus on practical strategies without understanding the spiritual realities, we would simply be creating another program or another method.

As we look at the state of the world in which we live and the current condition of the church, we will be asking many critical questions to learn what God's heart and will is and what He wants to do about the issues we face today. To help us do this, we also need to ask Him, as the Jews of His time did:

"What shall we do, that we may work the works of God?" (John 6:28, NKJV)

Pastor John Mulinde,
Pastor Mark Daniel,
and the WTM Missionaries

Prayer targets for week 1:

1. Ask the Lord to help you see the need of the hour
2. Spend time this week humbling yourself before God, asking Him to prepare you for this study

Audio/video link for week 1:

http://worldtrumpet.org/awakening-the-church
(week 1)

Lesson 1.

The State of the World and the Response of the Church

We have all seen the turmoil, problems, and crises that are going on around the globe and how they are perplexing even the wisest of the world leaders. They seem to be happening faster and faster, and each incidence seems to have a greater and greater impact on the world.

> The nations of the earth are being shaken, and it seems to be getting worse rather than better.

A recent example is the 7.0 magnitude earthquake that struck Haiti on January 12, 2010. The whole nation was shaken to its foundations. The Haitian government estimates that over 200,000 people died. In this nation, considered the poorest in the Western Hemisphere, with a population of nearly 9 million people, 2 million were left homeless and an estimated 3 million required emergency aid. Before the world could find viable answers and respond effectively, other crises occurred that stole its attention. A magnitude 8.8 earthquake occurred in Chile on February 27, 2010. Up to 80% of the population reported experiencing the tremors. The earthquake triggered a tsunami so strong that warnings were issued to 53 countries. Effects were felt on the coasts of San Diego, California and Tohoku, Japan. A few weeks later, on April 13, 2010, a magnitude 6.9 earthquake struck western China, killing over 2,200 people. In Yushu Province, over 85% of homes were destroyed.

The world barely had time to absorb that shock before the volcanic eruption in Iceland rocked Europe. In April 2010, the land of ice spewed out its fire, and the whole world was forced to stop and watch. Airports all across Europe were forced to close, causing millions of passengers to be stranded around the world. The International Air Transport Association estimated that the worldwide airline industry would suffer a $200 million loss each day that air traffic was disrupted.

The whole world was affected, not just Europe. Produce and other food exports, such as pineapple from Ghana; asparagus, broccoli, green beans, and flowers from Kenya; cod from Iceland; tuna from Vietnam and the Philippines; and mozzarella and fresh fruit from Italy, were spoiled, destroyed, or used to feed livestock because of the lack of flights. Undelivered car parts from Ireland and Germany delayed the production of cars in Japan and the United States.

A lot of shakings have been taking place in the earth. And it seems to be getting worse rather than better.

The table below lists just a few of the major events that have occurred worldwide in the first 10 years of the 21st century. (Please note that this is not all-inclusive; this table merely illustrates a few of the most devastating examples in each category.)

Global Catastrophic Events in Past 10 Years

NATURAL DISASTERS

Major earthquakes (>6.0 magnitude; some unmeasured):

- >550,000 reported killed; thousands of other deaths uncounted
- Millions left homeless and injured

Hurricanes, typhoons, cyclones, and major storms:

- Millions evacuated; millions without power
- >30,000 deaths
- >$86.5 billion in property damage from only two of these events

Flooding: >900,000 homeless; >500 killed

Miscellaneous:

- Wildfires in US and Australia: almost 200 killed and 500,000 evacuated
- Heat-wave in France: > 10,000 killed

WAR & TERRORISM

- September 2000: Beginning of Intifada (Palestinian uprising); over 4,000 killed in first 5 years
- October 2001: US begins military strike in Southern Afghanistan
- December 2002: North Korea reactivates nuclear plants
- March 2003: US launches war against Iraq
- October 2004: 70,000 reported dead in Darfur
- July 2006: Hezbollah kidnapping prompts war in Israel
- October 2006: North Korea starts nuclear testing
- August 2008: Georgia (Europe) under attack by Russian tanks
- December 2008: Israeli warplanes strike Gaza; at least 229 people killed
- February 2010: NATO launches major Afghan offensive

Terrorist attacks:

- September 11, 2001: terrorist attacks on the US; 2,967 killed victims and over 6,000 injured
- Terrorist bombings: almost 700 killed and over 300 injured
- Subway and rail blasts: over 200 killed

TRANSPORTATION DISASTERS

Plane crashes:

- Concorde crashes into a hotel in Gonesse, France; 113 killed
- American Airlines flight 587 crashes in New York; 265 killed
- Russian jetliner and cargo plane collide in air over southern Germany; 71 killed
- Plane crashes near Madrid, Spain; 153 killed

Miscellaneous

- Ferries sink in Gambia, Africa and in Red Sea; 2,903 killed
- Ship sinks in storm in East Asia; 600 missing

ILLNESS & DISEASES HAVING GLOBAL IMPACT IN PAST DECADE

- Mad cow disease
- SARS (severe acute respiratory syndrome)
- HIV/AIDS (1 in 5 adults in Africa living with HIV/AIDS)
- Bird flu
- Cholera (December 2008: deaths due to Zimbabwe pass 1,000)
- "Swine Flu" (H1N1)

ECONOMY

- December 2001: Enron files for bankruptcy
- October 2004: oil rises from $50 to $55 a barrel in <1 month
- July 2006: record oil price of $78.40 per barrel
- August 2007: world markets fall after US market decline
- July 2008: oil price per barrel reaches $147.02
- March 2009: International Monetary Fund reports global economy worst in 60 years
- April 2010: ash from Icelandic volcano closes European airports; effects entire world
- April 2010: Texas oil rig explodes; kills 11, devastates wildlife & coastlands; predicted $4.3 billion economic loss

In this time of need, what is the church doing to give direction?

"What should the church be doing to rise up and make Christ the hope of the nations?"

The Nations Are Being Shaken

The nations of the earth are being shaken. Fear and anxiety are increasingly gripping people in the nations as event after event brings death, chaos, trauma, fear, and ruin.

- The terrorist attacks on the US on September 11, 2001, shook the world; over 2,900 people lost their lives, and today the whole world still feels the effects and insecurity caused by the attacks.
- On December 16, 2004, a series of devastating tsunamis created by the over 9.0 magnitude undersea Indian Ocean earthquake killed over 230,000 people in 14 countries.
- Typhoon Wipha hit China on September 18, 2007. Although the death toll was quite low (14 were killed), 2 million people were evacuated, 13,000 homes were destroyed, 57,000 homes were damaged, and 100,000 hectares of farmland were inundated. Referred to as "the most destructive typhoon in a decade," damage was estimated to be about $1 billion.
- A "catastrophic" earthquake hit Haiti on January 12, 2010, causing an estimated 230,000 deaths, injuring 300,000, and leaving 1.2 million people needing emergency shelter.
- As of April 2010, in the "swine flu pandemic," at least 17,700 deaths worldwide have been attributed to H1N1

What should the church be doing to rise up and make Christ the hope of the nations?

The death toll from just these five events is almost half a million. That is almost 500,000 people killed; close to 500,000 families devastated.

Think of the grief, the trauma, the pain. The death of children, of mothers and fathers, of husbands and wives. These are just four events that have struck the world in the last 10 years; multiply the effects over and over and over again. The horror of loss, the horror of suffering, the pain, the anguish, the fear. And it is not just the deaths, there are multitudes injured in such events. In the recent Haiti earthquake, it has been estimated that 110,000 children alone were physically injured (roughly half the number of total injuries) and that mentions nothing of the emotional and psychological scars. And these events seem to be occurring with such rapidity.

The shakings stretch beyond the loss of life and limb to economic failures and financial losses; the loss of livelihoods that bring fear, depression, panic, despair, poverty, and ruin. Each disaster impacts individuals, families, communities, nations, and even continents. The global financial crisis of these past few years is continuing and the fight for survival seems to be getting more difficult. Bankruptcy, debt, and destitution are facing multitudes around the world; desperation, fear, and shame grasp hold of those who can no longer provide for their families.

The rate of suicide globally is increasing. Pornography, alcoholism, and drug and various other addictions are increasing, bringing their own devastating and shattering effects, but numbing the anxiety and fear momentarily. The internet is enabling the spread of pornography and the connection of criminal gangs, pedophiles, and human traffickers like never before.

A 2006 UN study of violence against children stated that in 2002, 150 million girls and 73 million boys under the age of 18 years experienced forced sexual intercourse or other forms of sexual violence. That is 223 million of one generation in 1 year whose lives are traumatized and affected by sexual abuse. While in the last century there was a sense of safety and innocence in childhood, with freedom to play in the streets and peace of mind for parents, now there is apprehension and fear and increasing levels of crime.

The "war on terror" and terrorist attacks in nation after nation around the world only heighten the pervading sense of worry, alarm, and disquiet that is creeping in on hearts and minds everywhere. With each bombing and attack, enhanced precautions are developed and introduced, making air travel increasingly difficult and tense. Disruptions to life are intensifying. Things are shaking.

Global financial assets, including stocks, bonds, and currencies, fell an estimated $50 trillion in 2008.

According to a March 9, 2009, article in Bloomberg (by Shamim Adam), the value of financial assets, including stocks, bonds, and currencies, fell an estimated $50 trillion in 2008. No nation in any part of the world was left untouched by this economic failure. Financial institutions collapsed, banks failed, housing markets were crushed, large corporations and even countries went bankrupt, and unemployment is higher then ever before (the US unemployment rate increased to 10.1% in October 2009, higher than it has been for over 25 years; while the unemployment rate in the Arab world is predicted to climb to 17% by the end of 2010). With many of its members on the verge of economic collapse, in May 2010, the European Union agreed to provide financial assistance to Eurozone states in difficulty.

Aren't these fears and terrors just going to increase in the coming days? In many nations, God is being pushed out, the church is having less of a voice, secularism is rising, and corruption in the church is frequently being reported.

Where is our hope? How will we stand as this anxiety and fear spreads and stretches us?

▸ **Exercise:**

Ponder each of these questions:

- What are the human solutions that are being offered?
- The academic solutions?
- The economic solutions?
- The environmental solutions?
- Are they solving anything?

Journal your thoughts in the margin, then be prepared to discuss this in your group.

What Is the Church Doing to Show That Christ Is the Hope of the Nations?

Is the church providing answers? As people are being stunned, traumatized, desensitized, and hardened, is the church providing direction? Is it revealing that Christ is the hope of the nations? As these shakings continue, is the church being relevant in its day?

God created the church to be many things. The church is to be the global, redeemed people of God

1. who do not live under the power of sin, the fallen nature, or Satan (Rom 6:6-7,10-11,22; 8:2-3, 13; Eph 2:2, Heb 9:14)
2. who are covenanted to God as His children and called by His name (John 1:12-13; Luke 20:36; Acts 3:25; Rom 8:14-17,23; 9:4; Gal 3:26,29; 4:5-6; Heb 2:14; 1 John 3:1-2; 5:18)
3. who are called out of the system and patterns of this world (John 15:19; 17:16; Rom 12:2; 1 John 3:1)
4. who are to reveal His glory, His love, His righteousness, and His Kingdom

authority on earth (John 13:35; 1 John 3:10,16; Col 3:4; 1 Peter 4:13; 5:1; 2 Cor 8:24)

The nations are not looking to the church for answers.

5. who are to fulfill His purposes among men (Acts 26:16; Rom 8:28; Eph 1:11; 3:10-11)
6. who are Christ's ambassadors, sent forth to reconcile the lost world to its Creator (2 Cor 5:18-20)
7. who comprise the army of God, sent into the earth to destroy the works of the devil and lead people out of the darkness and into the light (Acts 26:17-18; Heb 2:14)
8. who are corporately the Bride of Christ – called to be pure, spotless, and blameless – preparing Creation for the coming of the Day of the Lord (2 Cor 11:2; Rev 19:7; Phil 1:9-11)

The nations are not looking to the church for answers. Theyare pushing it into the corner, and in many nations, to a place of irrelevance. God has given a divine calling and position to the church to impact the nations, but at a time when the nations need it most, the church has not taken the power or position it has been given in Christ.

Therefore, we want to ask ourselves the question that will guide us through the entirety of these teachings: *"What must we do to do the works God requires?"* (John 6:28)

Time for Reflection:

What is the most meaningful statement or scripture you read today? ______

What does God want you to do in response to this? ______

As you pray your prayer target for this day/week, what are you feeling the Holy Spirit is saying or calling you to and what is the warfare coming against you? ______

At this point of our lesson, we want to enter into a time of prayer. This is an important part of our study each and every day. It is important that we don't just gather information and head knowledge; we want to come into the presence of the Spirit of God and take hold of the things He is revealing to us.

▸ **Time for Prayer:**

As we come to the end of lesson 1, it is important to realize the obvious fact that we are just beginning this journey. Although we may have loved the Lord for a long time and may have prayed many prayers, we are seeing by the very things we just discussed that we need to enter into a different place so that we may see different results. The way we want to approach this first week of prayer in particular is to realize that we need to ask the Lord just to *begin* to change our hearts, our mindsets, and our ways. We want to begin to ask the Lord to lead us out of where we are and into the place that He wants us to be. We know we need to repent, and we may even have a deep desire to repent, but we might not yet see how to really do it. That's okay. This is where we begin to cry out for His mercy and trust in His grace. We ask Him to bring a spirit of humility and repentance. He is faithful.

Lesson 2:
Are the Heavens Open or Closed?

When Jesus Christ was beginning His ministry, He went to the river Jordan to be baptized by John. When John first saw Jesus, he hesitated to baptize Him, but Jesus said, "Let it be so now; It is proper for us to do this to fulfill all righteousness" (Matthew 3:15). In other words, Jesus was saying, "If my mission is to be accomplished, I need to take every step in the process my Father has determined for Me."

> You are my Son, whom I love; with you I am well pleased.
> Luke 3:21-22

Open Heavens

As he was baptizing others in the Jordan, John saw Jesus walking along and remarked, "Behold! The Lamb of God… I did not know Him, but He who sent me ... said to me, 'Upon whom you see the Spirit descending, and remaining on Him, this is He who baptizes with the Holy Spirit'" (John 1:29-33, NKJV). The Bible says the day Jesus was baptized He came up out of the waters and prayed, and "heaven was opened and the Holy Spirit descended on him in bodily form like a dove. And a voice came from heaven: 'You are my Son, whom I love; with you I am well pleased'" (Luke 3:21-22).

▸ Exercise:

Read John 1:43-51.

In verse 50, what did Jesus say they would see? ______________________

____

In verse 51, what did Jesus say they would see? ______________________

____

It is easy to pass over this passage without understanding what Jesus was really saying. He did not say, "You are going to see many great things, such as the lame walking, the blind seeing, the deaf hearing, thousands being fed, or the dead being raised." Instead, He said, "You are going to see greater things than that. You are going to see the heavens opened and the angels of God ascending and descending on the Son of Man."

What was Jesus referring to when He said to Nathaniel, "Greater things are you going to see"? He was saying, "You are going to see the gates of heaven open! You are going to see what it means for God to dwell among His people. All those other things – the dead rising, the blind seeing, thousands being fed – are simply the fruits of God's presence coming upon His people. This is what Jesus spoke about when He told us to pray, "Your Kingdom come, your will be done on earth as it is in heaven" (Matthew 6:10).

There are many places in the Bible that provide evidence of God's presence being among His people:

- Jacob at the altar in Bethel seeing angels ascending and descending from heaven (Gen 28:11-12) and struggling with the Angel of the Lord (Gen 32:24-30)
- The pillar of fire leading the children of Israel through the Red Sea (Ex 14:19-25) and for 40 years in the wilderness (Ex 13:21-22; Num 9:15, 14:14; Deut 1:32-33, Neh 9:12,19)
- God's presence to win the battle as Moses had his arms raised (Ex 17:8-16)
- The ark of the covenant giving them victory in battle (Josh 6:1-20) and parting the Jordan River (Josh 3:6-17)
- Jesus with the disciples in Jerusalem, giving them power and authority to do His work (Luke 9:1-2; Matt 10:1)
- The early church spreading the Gospel in the nations and turning cities upside down with the power given to them through the Holy Spirit (Acts 4:31; Rom 15:18-21; 1 Thess 1:4-5; 1 Cor 2:1-5; 1Peter 1:12)

▶ **Exercise:**

Choose one of lines a to f above and read each of the verses listed. In these examples, how did the presence of God impact the earth?__________

____

____

When the heavens were opened, we saw Jesus' presence being among the people, His authority in His teaching and work, Him healing and delivering. We saw God at work and moving among the people. The early church had unity, turned cities upside down, and the power of the Holy Spirit and the presence of God filled the church. The heavens were open!

When the heavens are opened, you see God's presence actively impacting what goes on in the land.

Closed Heavens

We should also note that if the Bible teaches that the heavens can be opened, it means they can also be closed. Does the Bible mention closed heavens? And when the heavens are closed, what are the conditions among men that caused this?

There are many scriptures in the Bible that speak of the heavens being closed. A "covering" over the nations is mentioned in Isaiah 25:7. Ezekiel 32:7-8 says the Lord sometimes darkens the heavens over the land, Isaiah 59:2 says the Lord will hide His face from us, and in 2 Chronicles 7:13, God says, "When I shut up the heavens...or command locusts to devour the land or send a plague among my people." The scriptures show that God, in fact, sometimes does close the heavens; and when He does, evil floods into the land. Darkness thrives. The devil then comes to kill, steal, and destroy.

Do we live in a day and time when we primarily see the heavens open or we primarily see the heavens closed? Are we seeing

- Victory upon victory?
- God routing our enemies?
- Uncrossable seas parted?
- Power & authority?
- Divine enablement & provision?

▸ Exercise:

A lot of scriptures describe closed heavens and open heavens. For each of the scriptures below, check off all those that happen when darkness comes and the heavens are closed.

2 Chronicles 7:13: "At times I might shut up the heavens so that no rain falls, or command grasshoppers to devour your crops, or send plagues among you."

Check all that apply for 2 Chronicles 7:13:

____ drought ____ earthquakes
____ locusts ____ crops fail
____ flood ____ plagues

Haggai 1:9-12: "You hoped for rich harvests, but they were poor. And when you brought your harvest home, I blew it away... It's because of you that the heavens withhold the dew and the earth produces no crops. I have called for a drought on your fields and hills—a drought to wither the grain and grapes and olive trees and all your other crops, a drought to starve you and your livestock and to ruin everything you have worked so hard to get."

Check all that apply for Haggai 1:9-10:

____ drought	____ crops fail
____ locusts	____ starvation
____ laboring in vain	____ poor harvests

Isaiah 59:1-2: Surely the arm of the Lord is not too short to save, nor his ear too dull to hear. But your iniquities have separated you from your God; your sins have hidden his face from you, so that he will not hear.

Check all that apply for Isaiah 59:1-2:

____ hindered prayer	____ drought of His presence
____ hail	____ earthquakes
____ flood	____ loss of communion with God

Are we, today, experiencing droughts, floods, locusts, plagues, starvation? Do you see signs of closed heavens? What about the flood of pornography from the internet? What about our children's purity and faith being eaten away by the world system? What about the plagues of immorality, the poor harvest among the work of God, starvation for God's presence, the inundation of wickedness? God is being pushed out of society and we are seeing the darkness coming in like a flood.

▶ **Reflection:**

In your nation, are you seeing that the heavens are more open or more closed? ____________ Explain your answer: ______________________________

____

____

When I shut up the heavens so that there is no rain, or command locusts to devour the land or send a plague among my people, if my people, who are called by my name, will humble themselves and pray and seek my face and turn from their wicked ways, then will I hear from heaven and will forgive their sin and will heal their land.
2 Chronicles 7:13-14

We Must Cry Out to the One Who Closed the Heavens

Let us also remember one thing: the devil has no power to shut the heavens himself. The Bible tells us who closes the heavens. It is our Father. He says, "When I shut up the heavens..." (2 Chronicles 7:13). That means before we command the enemy to leave, to let go, to open up the heavens, we need to go to the Father, who allowed the heavens to be closed in the first place. We would do better to humble ourselves and pray and seek His face (2 Chronicle 7:14), and ask Him, "What is it that caused You to close us off?" He is the

One who says, "Surely the arm of the Lord is not too short to save, nor his ear too dull to hear. But your iniquities have separated you from your God; your sins have hidden his face from you, so that he will not hear" (Isaiah 59:1-2). So, before we can use authority against the enemy, against the locust, or against the plagues, we need to go to the One who was so offended in the first place that He shut the heavens and allowed the enemy to gain control. All this is part of the stages and process that lead to opening the heavens.

Time for Reflection:

What is the most meaningful statement or scripture you read today? ______________________________

What does God want you to do in response to this? ______________________________

As you pray your prayer target for this day/week, what are you feeling the Holy Spirit is saying or calling you to and what is the warfare coming against you? ______________________________

▸ Time for Prayer:

Today, let us ask for a heart of humility and repentance. Let your heart cry out to the Living God, the God who has the only authority to open the heavens over you. Cry out that the Holy Spirit would lead you into all truth. As we have been made aware that there is more evidence of closed heavens than open heavens, as we begin to see the state of things differently, ask God to begin to open the heavens over your life. Cry out that the Holy Spirit would lead you deeper into the light as He begins to peal away the layers of darkness covering our eyes.

Please listen to the following link, which is a recording of a prayer time that took place in Uganda during the Mission Open Heaven Training in April-May 2010: http://worldtrumpet.org/awakening-the-church (week 1 prayer time).

Listening to this prayer time will encourage you and help you press into the place where God wants to draw you. There is a spirit of repentance and of deepening humility in this prayer time so as you listen,
ask the Holy Spirit

- to stir humility,
- to let your heart be fully engaged in the spirit of repentance that is taking place, and
- to guide you deeper into humility and contrition, that He may take you out of where you have been and into the place that He desires you to be.

Lesson 3:
Why Awaken? Time Is Growing Late

Another reason why we were told to abandon ourselves to God and to wake up is because the time is growing late; the Day of the Lord's return is near. And scriptures tell us that as the time grows late, things will grow more intense. These last days we are living in were foretold. The Bible predicts there would be many things that would come to devour the people of God. It says that many will fall away, even some of the faithful (Matthew 24:10). Jesus said the deception would even be targeted at the elect, to pull them away if possible (Mark 13:22).

There are numerous predictions about what will come and how it will affect people as time is getting late. There are forecasts of the deceptions that would come, and the wounds and sins that would pierce people's hearts, causing their love to grow cold and many to fall away.

▸ **Exercise:**

Read the following verses. List things that God says will happen as time draws later.

Matthew 24:4,9-14

2 Timothy 3:1-5

Luke 21:8-19,34

An honest look at what is happening around the world today shows us that we are encountering more than just physical crises. There is a growing coldness to the things of God, if not even a rage. More and more, people are becoming lovers of self and living selfishly. If we include the spiritual reality inside the church of Christ – the unbelief, the doubt, the weak faith, the scandals, the shortcomings, the level of sin, the rhetoric without the reality, the failure to meet the standards of God's Word – we realize that many Biblical prophecies regarding the end times are unfolding. The deception and darkness is already devouring many souls. Many do not know Christ, and every day that passes, people are getting harder, they are getting more cynical, they are weakening, and they do not have the power to repent or believe.

> Slumber is an awareness of our need, but an inability to do anything about it.

The Spirit of Slumber

Another thing that we will experience in the latter days is the spirit of slumber. The scriptures present that as time grows later, there is going to be an increasing divide between two groups of people. There will be those who are being caught in the current of what is taking place in the world and those who are seeking to "live holy and godly lives" as we look forward to the day of His coming and that we ought to "make every effort to be found spotless, blameless, and at peace with him" (2 Peter 3:12,14). There are two types of people; those who are going to be scoffing and thinking, "What's the big deal?" and who are caught up in going with their own evil desires, and those people making every effort to be right with God, seeking Him, and walking with Him. As time grows later, this divide is growing wider and wider. There are those getting caught up with what is going on in the culture and those who are beginning to seek after God like never before. This is the reason that Jesus tells us we must not be caught unaware (Mark 13:33). As time grows later, we will see an increase in the spirit of slumber that will keep us from pursuing God.

One of the greatest enemies during this time is slumber. Because the divide is pushing things further and further, we're going to find that we aren't able to be alert or to be found ready. Slumber is a strong force that is coming in and giving us a sense of powerlessness, prayerlessness, and lethargy; therefore, not only are we not we fighting the slumber, we also are not fighting the darkness that is coming in.

▶ **Exercise:**

Read 2 Peter 3:3-14 and 1 Thessalonians 5:1-9. What kind of people do we need to be? ______________________________________

____

____

A spirit of slumber begins to settle on people. It gets thick in such a way that you can see it, layer upon layer. As the years go by, you can see the slumber thickening.

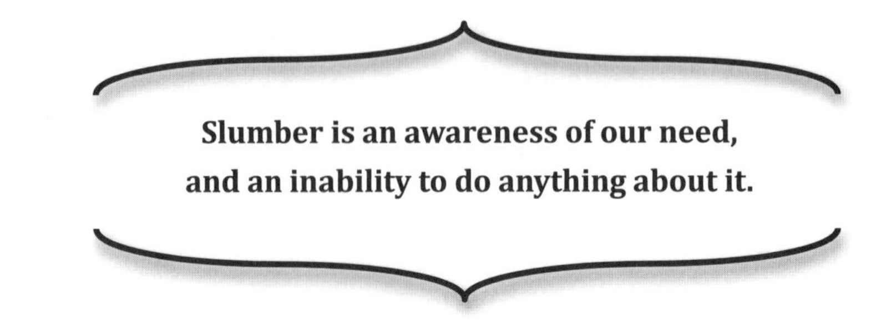

Slumber is an awareness of our need, and an inability to do anything about it.

We see the problems in the world and our own lives, and either

- we're numb and unmoved,
- we have a faith that is too small to rise up and change anything,
- we feel like a victim,
- we have no hope, or
- we have no vision or power to go forward.

We see what is happening around us, but we don't have the strength to rise up and do anything about it.

This means the enemy can deceive us and take us captive to push us back and weaken our faith. This brings us to the place where we do not rise up to resist and fight. All around us, in our cities, communities, and families, there are many people, including ourselves, who are falling into places of slumber and being deceived. In many ways, we begin to feel more and more powerless. We even see the church being pushed into a place of irrelevance in many nations. Christians are losing hope, strength, and courage; in other words, they are growing weaker as the darkness increases.

Children and youth are being destroyed all around us. We don't even need the news media to tell us that. We see it with our own eyes. We see families being destroyed and marriages falling apart. We see children becoming worldly and being spoiled by lack of family discipline and overindulgence. We see a lost generation that is helpless to save itself. And in such a situation, we need to ask ourselves, *"What shall we do, that we may work the works of God?"*

How Does This Affect Us Personally?

Let's look at this from a personal perspective. Look at what the Word says will be happening in people's lives as time grows later.

▶ **Exercise:**

Review your answers in the 2 Timothy 3:1-5 box above.
Which of these things are particularly affecting you and pulling on you?

____

____

____

Do you rise up and seek to overcome or do you just accept it? ________

____

____

When you open your eyes and see in the Spirit, you cannot help being gripped by a sense of urgency and desperation. This should stir within us the heart cry that we see in Luke 21:34-36: "Oh God, preserve me from this evil generation!" The scriptures tell us many people will suffer a shipwreck of their faith and fall into deception (1 Timothy 1:19). As time grows later, the intensity against our walk with Christ will only increase, and we need to rise up, resist, and fight.

What I'm trying to say, brethren, is that it has been prophesied that in the last days there will be apostasy, there will be deception, there will be falling away, there will be slumber, there will be a drawing away from God, there will be a counterfeit life, a form of godliness but denying the power. We need to cry out to awaken and see God, not only for ourselves, but also for our nation.

Time for Reflection:

What is the most meaningful statement or scripture you read today? ______________________

What does God want you to do in response to this? ______________________

As you pray your prayer target for this day/week, what are you feeling the Holy Spirit is saying or calling you to and what is the warfare coming against you? ______________________

▶ **Time for Prayer:**

As you go into your time with the Lord today, continue to ask for

- a deepening level of humility,
- a continued awareness of needing to repent at deeper levels, and
- a heart cry to be taken out of every form of darkness, especially the spirit of slumber.

Ask the Lord to strengthen you in the Way so that you may continue to see the things that are hindering Him from flowing the fullness of His life through you. Let the Lord continue to stir a depth of humility and repentance in you. We need to see the things that He wants to expose so that as the enemy is coming in like a flood, we may stand more deeply and firmly in Christ — the One who is Lord over the flood (Psalm 29:3).

Lesson 4:
Awaken and Rise Up, Army of God

We are seeing that the hour is late; that there is increasing trauma, turbulence, and trouble in the world in which we live; that there is a reality to the heavens being open or being closed; and that we as the church are not yet prepared or ready for the times and challenges that are coming.

> Blow the trumpet in Zion; sound the alarm on my holy hill. Let all who live in the land tremble, for the day of the LORD is coming. It is close at hand — a day of darkness and gloom.
> Joel 1:1-2

There is a battle, a war between darkness and light, which is taking place. This is the war that Jesus spoke of, saying, "To him who overcomes, I will give reward." It is not a war we choose; it is a war that chooses us. You don't turn it away and say, "I don't want that kind of battle. I want another one." This is a war that will choose you, and sometimes we don't have the option to pull back. We have to go forward and overcome.

There is a Call to Raise an Army in These Last Days

> Joel 1:1-2: "Blow the trumpet in Zion; sound the alarm on my holy hill. Let all who live in the land tremble, for the day of the LORD is coming. It is close at hand - a day of darkness and gloom, a day of clouds and blackness. Like dawn spreading across the mountains a large and mighty army comes, such as never was of old nor ever will be in ages to come."

All over the world God is raising up a remnant (an army). God is calling a people to Himself who will set themselves apart from the world and allow Him to work within them to prepare them for the times ahead, times of great trials and temptations! We have seen that in the coming days many people will fall and betray their faith. No one will endure through the trials unless they are sustained by the Lord Himself. But God is raising a people about whom He says, "Those who know their God shall be strong, and shall carry out great exploits" (Daniel 11:32). God is preparing these vessels to raise the standard in the nations and declare that His Spirit will intervene. And He has promised that, "When the enemy shall come in like a flood, My Spirit will raise a standard" (Isaiah 59:19). And His army is that standard. Hallelujah!

The army has an opposition: the enemy. There are many spiritual forces of darkness that come against us in this war, growing ever darker and more aggressive, and seeking to take us out of the battle, to destroy us, and make us ineffective.

Slumber is one of these spiritual forces of darkness that has many effects; one is that it keeps us from rising up in the power of Christ and advancing the purposes of God. As time draws later, this force will increase. When human nature finds something too hard to confront, the tendency is to pull back and postpone confrontation, to put it off, to do the easier things first. But we need to look at how much time we have. Beloved, the hour is late; the Day of the Lord is around the corner. Jesus warned us that we must

- Be found ready (Matt 24:44, 25:10, Luke 12:35,38,40&47)
- Not be caught unaware (Matt 24:39, Luke 21:34)
- Pray that we will be alert (Mark 13:33)

The Parable of the Ten Virgins

At that time the kingdom of heaven will be like ten virgins who took their lamps and went out to meet the bridegroom. Five of them were foolish and five were wise. The foolish ones took their lamps but did not take any oil with them. The wise, however, took oil in jars along with their lamps. The bridegroom was a long time in coming, and they all became drowsy and fell asleep. At midnight the cry rang out: 'Here's the bridegroom! Come out to meet him!' Then all the virgins woke up and trimmed their lamps. The foolish ones said to the wise, 'Give us some of your oil; our lamps are going out.' 'No,' they replied, 'there may not be enough for both us and you. Instead, go to those who sell oil and buy some for yourselves.' But while they were on their way to buy the oil, the bridegroom arrived. The virgins who were ready went in with him to the wedding banquet. And the door was shut. Later the others also came. 'Sir! Sir!' they said. 'Open the door for us!' But he replied, 'I tell you the truth, I don't know you.' Therefore keep watch, because you do not know the day or the hour.

Matthew 25:1-13

▶ Exercise:

Read **Matthew 25:1-13:** What was the difference between the wise virgins and the foolish virgins? ______________________

____
____
____
____
____

What were the consequences for the foolish virgins?______________________

____
____
____
____
____

What does the oil symbolize? ______________

____
____
____
____
____

All of the virgins slumbered, but at some point there was a wake-up call: "The bridegroom is coming; wake up!"

This is the time of the wake-up call. This is the time of separating the wise from the foolish. Some people will not change; they're going to remain foolish and obstinate. They will continue in their ways. 2 Thessalonians 2:11 says that because they refuse to believe the truth, the Lord will send them a powerful delusion so they will believe a lie.

At 4:00am in the USA, a 26-year-old man rises from his bed and begins to read the Bible. He will read and pray until around 6.30am, when he meets with the other young men living in his home, a house in a crime-ridden area of a large city, to worship, pray, and fellowship around the Word until 8:00am, when they head to work. In the evenings he will often pray and fellowship with other believers, men and women hungry for God, as he leads a house church.

Four years ago, already a Christian, he began to hear the call to awaken and arise at AfriCamp and his heart responded "Yes!" He took the message seriously and started to allow the Lord to consecrate and set his life apart for Him. As he did so, he saw the Lord exposing and stripping away things in his life, revealing human effort, hidden idolatry, and deeply entrenched mind-sets.

In yielding and allowing God to work in him, he began to witness God doing what only He could do: drawing youth from the neighborhood to the house through prayer, seeing darkness pushed back in his own life and in the lives of his family, and awakening others around him, a remnant being gathered together to battle.

The distinction between those who know their God, who seek Him and trust in Him, and those who are deluded, deceived, and slumbering, is ever widening. Human efforts are failing to solve the problems of our world. Today we see the enemy coming in like a flood. He is flooding the nations, flooding the church, flooding families, flooding whole societies with his works. In only a short time, we have been forced to lower our standards. The enemy is flooding in; that tells us that it is time for the Lord to raise His standard. We want to come to a place where we can see that this is not about choosing a good thing to do; this is God's way of dealing with the issues that are perplexing humanity. We must ask,

"What shall we do, that we may work the works of God?"

God is Calling Out His People

There are men and women all across the nations who have heard the call of the Lord to be set apart, to awaken, to arise. While many have chosen to procrastinate and rest in vain excuses, there are those who have already started the walk, who are taking up their positions in this end time army. They have counted the cost and concluded that God is worth more to them than the attractions of this present age.

If we are going to be vessels God can use in this generation, we all need to

A lady in Kenya, once a businesswoman, kneels on the dusty floor of a small meeting room to pray. Over the last year she has known and encountered God in ways she never imagined she would and has perceived Him drawing her and leading her as she has given herself to seeking Him in prayer. During the day she gathers with others from the town to pray and cry out for God's purposes, sometimes for 6 or 7 hours at a time; at other times, she serves the community with her gift of administration, depending on the Lord for His provision.

A number of years ago she was in slumber, unaware of the lateness of the times she was living in and oblivious of her calling and destiny, but she sensed a stirring of dissatisfaction with the status quo and a desire for reality in the church and in her life. As she determined to seek God, He was faithful to His word and drew near to her, awakening her and raising her up, teaching her to pray and fight for His kingdom to be established on earth as it is in heaven. Now she sees God moving in her community to bring reviving and observes Him opening doors that she could never have opened so that she is even able to share the "Trumpet Call" on television.

fall before God and say, "God, have mercy upon me! I can see my life described in some of the scriptures I have read over the last few days, and I don't want to believe popular theology. I don't want to wait until that Day to prove who is right. I want to start today. Not only for my life, but for the nations. I want to be the true church that is carrying the Great Commission to go to the nations and make disciples of every nation. I want to go and teach the nations what Christ teaches." We need to step out of the status quo and abandon ourselves to the Lord to be equipped and prepared for the challenges that are in front of us. We, as the church, need to be crying out, "God, how can You work through us and in us as You did in the Bible?"

God is raising an army: an army with the ability to send out the message, to speak a clear warning message to the nations that will cause people to arise and flee from the wrath of God. This army knows the time is short and they are given totally to the call of their Captain. They are selfless people who avail themselves as yielded vessels and let God do what He will with them.

A teacher travels 10 kilometers to join with other believers in the home of a couple in continental Europe. The husband and wife, who were impacted by the wake-up call several years ago, established an altar of prayer in their home that has gradually attracted and drawn many others.

Before their children awake, they meet at 4:00am to pray, read the Word, and devote themselves to God; their children then join them, along with their fellow church members, for worship and prayer before the workday begins. In the evenings, they also gather daily to seek the Lord for a few hours, keeping the fire burning and pushing back the darkness.

Prior to having their hearts awakened to God's purposes and desires, they were church-goers ignorant of the battle and unconscious of the spiritual war taking place, but God has roused them and is using them in their city and nation to raise up the level of prayer and turn hearts back to God.

We are called to this army. You are called to this army. It is not an army that can be distracted, hindered, or defeated, because the fire of the Lord goes with them.

Time for Reflection:

What is the most meaningful statement or scripture you read today? ______________________

What does God want you to do in response to this? ______________________

As you pray your prayer target for this day/week, what are you feeling the Holy Spirit is saying or calling you to and what is the warfare coming against you? ______________________

▶ Time for Prayer:

Today we need to set aside at least an hour to 90 minutes to spend before the Lord. After praying all week for the Lord to even begin to bring the level of humility and repentance required, we trust that He has been faithful. Take the time with God. You may need to go for a walk in a remote place where you can cry out or you might need to stay in your prayer closet, but this time needs to be given for the Lord to take you deeper and further.

We have seen that

- what we have been doing is clearly not accomplishing the works of God,
- the world turns to the world and not to the church for help and so-called "solutions" for the problems of the day,
- we are not living under open heavens, and
- we are in a state of slumber.

We have seen these things and so much more as we have let the Lord open our eyes to the state of the church and of our own lives. As our hearts have been humbled by these things and as the Holy Spirit has brought conviction about the state of our own lives in relation to the standards of God, let us continue to cry out for a deep level of humility. Cry out to see the Lord for who He is and for what He wants to do. Cry out and tell God that you no longer want to stay where you are, but that you want to be where He wants you to be, no matter what that looks likes. We want to be vessels through which He may flow. Cry out to be a part of the remnant—a part of the army that God is raising up across the nations of this world.

Week 2.

How Do We Do the Work God Requires?

GOAL OF THE WEEK:

This week we want to
1. To understand the difference between doing good works and fulfilling the will of God
2. To surrender ourselves to doing the heart and will of God

I felt called to ministry in my teenage years. I had a great burden to abandon everything to Christ and to see Him move in the lives of people. I studied the Bible in college, then went to seminary to for more training.

I started pastoring a church in my early 20s. I was doing everything that was out there, all the programs and strategies of the day, but was frustrated and discouraged because I was not seeing the breakthroughs my heart was burdened to see. The impact in the city was small; even the impact in the church was lacking. Many times, the addictions, problems, and struggles in the church were just as great as what I saw in the world. But I kept hoping.

For more than 15 years I kept trying every new strategy or teaching that came along. I spent thousands of dollars on conferences, books, CDs, and programs. I even tried new worship styles, small group models, and new spiritual emphases. I'd follow a new program for about 6 or 9 months, maybe a year, then I'd realize that we were back where we started; we hadn't moved ahead in any real way. It felt like we were wandering.

I eventually lost all hope. I was either going to quit ministry or God had to show me the way to do His work the way you see it done in the Bible. I remember reading about people like Elijah, Elisha, Moses, and others, and I seeing the power God worked through them, the clarity of their understanding of their mission, and the way God spoke to them and led them in everything. I didn't have that. I had been following programs, not God, and I became desperate to know the God revealed in the Bible.

I began to surrender absolutely everything I could to follow Him. I was so aware that I didn't know the God who is revealed in scriptures, but that's the God I hungered for. I wanted to know how to do His work, not just have a church job or just run a church program. I wanted to know: *How do I do the work that God requires?*

As God began dealing with me and I began letting go of control of my life, He started to strip away my self-life and self-effort, and I started to see what it really meant to entrust myself to him. In that time of abandoning myself and following Him—no longer following a method or program, but following the person of Jesus Christ, willing to lay down everything He required of me—He began to bring me into a work much bigger than I had ever been able to do. It was His work, and He opened doors, brought insight and revelation. Every piece began to come together for the work of God to go forward. I saw Him doing work through me that I could never do myself, and I began to realize that He really can do His work through us if we give Him our lives.

— Pastor Mark Daniel

Prayer targets for week 2:

1. What must I do to do the work that God requires?
2. How do I believe in the One He sent?

Audio/video link for week 2:

http://worldtrumpet.org/awakening-the-church
(week 2)

Lesson 1.
Fulfilling the Will of God

The work of God is this: to believe in the One he has sent.
John 6:29

Let's focus on the question Jesus was asked in John 6:28: *"What must we do to do the works God requires?"*

In a time like this, in an age that is perplexing human wisdom, what *must* we do to do the work God requires of us? To tap into the roots – the answer – to our question, we need to understand the answer Jesus gave. When they asked Him, "What shall we do, that we may work the works of God?" (John 6:28), He answered, "The work of God is this: to believe in the One he has sent" (John 6:29).

To believe in this One that the Lord sent to us, we must trust and follow Him as best we can. We must follow His example, and work and act and think and obey – serve and love the Lord our God – in the same way that Jesus did.

How did Jesus serve the Lord? He determined to do the Father's will—**full stop** (Matthew 7:21). He did only what He saw the Father doing (John 5:19); He said only what the Father told Him to say (John 12:49-50). This is what is required to do the works of God.

What Is Required?

To see how to do the work God requires, we need to abandon the presumption that certain activities make up the ministry of God. Our Christian activities, though they may be good, are not necessarily what will fulfill the desire of God's heart. As we begin to strip away these presumptions, we begin to move more closely to understanding what is the work that God requires.

In Matthew 7:21-23, Jesus said, "Not everyone who says to me, 'Lord, Lord,' will enter the kingdom of heaven, but only he who does the will of my Father who is in heaven. Many will say to me on that day, 'Lord, Lord, did we not prophesy in Your name, and in Your name drive out demons and perform many miracles?' Then I will tell them plainly, 'I never knew you. Away from me, you evildoers!'"

> Doing the work God requires is not just doing good activity; it is fulfilling the heart desires of the Father.

In our simple understanding of ministry, these people were saying, "Didn't we minister in Your name? Didn't we serve You? Didn't we do what You required of us?" But Jesus said, "No. Get out of my sight you evildoers." Although they preached, prophesied, and worked miracles in His name, He thought of them as evildoers. Jesus said they would not enter the kingdom of heaven because they were not doing the will of the Father.

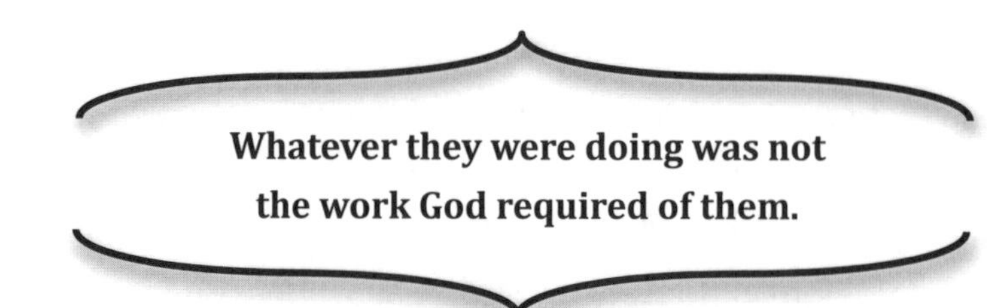

Whatever they were doing was not the work God required of them.

Jesus makes it clear that not everyone will enter heaven, "but only he who does the will of my Father who is in Heaven" (Matthew 7:21). In other words, "The will of My Father is the desire of His heart: that which He wants to see accomplished and how He wants to see it accomplished."

▸ Exercise:

What is the difference between (1) doing good activity and (2) doing and fulfilling the will of God? ____________________________________

____

____

Doing the work God requires is not just doing good activity; **it is fulfilling the heart desires of the Father.**

The work God requires is not just any good thing done in any way; it is doing the will of God, His way.

Read Joshua 1.

Did God have a clear will and mission to accomplish (vv 3-5)? __________

What was it?____

____

____

What would be the result if Joshua had done something other than what God required? ____

____

____

Did the Lord give the Israelites clear direction for how to do this work (vv 6-9)? ______________ What was it? ________________________________

____

____

What was the result when they joined God on His mission and did it His way (Joshua 21:43-45)? ____________________________

____

____

So the Lord gave Israel all the land he had sworn to give their forefathers, and they took possession of it and settled there. The Lord gave them rest on every side, just as he had sworn to their forefathers. Not one of their enemies withstood them; the Lord handed all their enemies over to them. Not one of all the Lord's good promises to the house of Israel failed; every one was fulfilled.
Joshua 21:43-45

God gave Joshua the mission to go and take the Promised Land. God told him how to do it and promised that everywhere Joshua put his foot, God would give Joshua that land. God promised to be with Joshua as He had been with Moses. Because Joshua and the Israelites did all that the Lord had commanded, "not one of their enemies withstood them" and "not one of all the Lord's good promises...failed; every one was fulfilled" (Joshua 21:43-45).

The work God requires is not just serving God in a leadership role; it is recognizing the desires of the Father's heart, then submitting to and fulfilling them.

Read I Samuel 15.

What did God require of Saul (vv 1-3)? ____________________________

____

____

Did Saul do work for God? ________ Was it what God required? _________

What was God's response to the work Saul had done for him (v 10)?_____

____

____

Saul, in his human thinking, felt that he had fully followed the directions the Lord had given. Many of us would have done—and truthfully, probably have done—the same thing. However, because he did not obey the word of the Lord and complete the mission the Lord had given him, the kingdom was taken from him and given to another.

The work God requires is not just using human thinking and effort to do ministry; it is listening to the voice of God, and following the instructions that He gives.

Read Judges 7:1-8,16-25.

What were the directions God gave to Gideon and his army (vv 3-7,16-20)?______________________________________

____

____

Were these instructions clear? ________ Did Gideon follow them? _______

What was the result (v 22, Judges 8:28)? ________________________________

____

____

God gave very clear and specific directions to Gideon, and Gideon and his men trusted the Lord and followed those instructions exactly. Even though it did not make sense to their human reasoning to reduce the size of their army to 300 men, they did it. Even though it seemed foolish, they took their trumpets and jars into the battle, and then they watched the Lord bring the victory. A small army of 300 men defeated an army of 135,000 by obeying their God and doing exactly what He told them.

Doing the Will of God

We come to a place where we're not just doing activities for God or trying to serve God the best we can, but we want to do His will, we want to know His heart, and we want to fulfill His heart's desire. Doing anything else is unacceptable.

> But now your kingdom will not endure; the Lord has sought out a man after his own heart and appointed him leader of his people, because you have not kept the Lord's command.
> 1 Samuel 13:14

Joshua did exactly what God said. He prayed, he did not accept fear or discouragement in his heart, he meditated on the Word, he kept the things before the people. Saul did not. It looked like a small thing that Saul did; it is probably something we would all do. He didn't fully obey what God had said; he did things his own way. He followed his own thoughts; what he did was unauthorized. Then God said "I am going to look for a man who has My heart's desire" (1 Samuel 13:14), and He took the kingdom from him and gave it to David.

Time for Reflection:

What is the most meaningful statement or scripture you read today? ______________________

What does God want you to do in response to this? ______________________

As you pray your prayer target for this day/week, what are you feeling the Holy Spirit is saying or calling you to and what is the warfare coming against you? ______________________

▶ Time for Prayer:

The question that will remain before us is one that we will begin taking to the Lord in prayer: *What must I do that I may do the work that God requires?* Ask the Lord to open your eyes and your understanding. Ask Him to begin to make a clear distinction in your heart between doing good activities and fulfilling the desire of the God's heart. In humility and contrition before the throne, ask the Lord to show you how to walk in the "answer" to that question: to *believe* in the One that He sent.

Lesson 2.

Asking God to Reveal His Heart's Desires

Fulfilling the desire of God's heart is what matters, not doing right or good activities.

God is at work. He has a mission. If you and I do not seek to know His heart, it will not stop Him from working and it will not stop Him from accomplishing what He wants to do. But it will hinder us from being fruitful, effective, and fulfilled.

We therefore cannot ignore God's heart cry. It is our duty, as servants of God, to make His heart's desire our purpose and to see His mission accomplished. We need to set out to fulfill His will (objectives, goals, desires, etc) or everything else we do will distance us from God's true work. We cannot afford to just sail through life, following the trends, methods, or latest programs that come our way. We need to crave and cry out for God's heart, God's mission, and God's ways.

Fulfilling the desire of God's heart is what matters, not doing right or good activities.

▶ **Exercise:**

Read 1 Corinthians 3:10-15.

How must the work of God be done (v 10)? ______________________

____

____

Are there right and wrong ways to do the work? ________________

What are the consequences? ______________________________

____

____

The emphasis of these scriptures is that we must be careful what we do in the service of God because our works will be tested on that Day. They will be passed through fire to test the quality of our work. Some works will not survive, and the person who produced them will suffer loss and his lifetime of work will have been wasted. Other works will survive, and that person will receive a reward.

Man's Ways Versus God's Ways

Many times, we're just doing the work the way our culture does it. We don't realize how often we take on the ways of our culture, but those ways are not God's ways and they are not acceptable to Him. A lot of times, we're doing work the way people do it, but it's not fruitful and it's not even going to stand on that final Day. Look at the difference between doing things man's way and God's way:

Man's Ways

- Trusts self; is self-reliant, self-sufficient
- Wants to maintain control, do things his own way
- Wants to prove he is right
- Has a demanding spirit
- Is protective of time, things, self
- Desires success
- Is driven by recognition & approval
- Is wounded when not promoted
- Thinks of what he can do for God
- Feels confident in how much he knows
- Want God so he can be more successful
- Works to maintain image
- Is self-conscious
- Compares self to others ("I'm not so bad")
- Seeks to do the work in his own ability
- Doesn't spend much time with God
- Doesn't spend much time in the Word or prayer
- Doesn't ache with God's heart desires
- Doesn't carry God's burdens

God's Ways

- Is dependant on God, believes God
- Sees his neediness
- Surrenders control, trusts God, wants & longs for God's will
- Is willing to lay down his rights
- Has a gracious heart and spirit
- Denies self; serves and extends himself to others
- Wants to please God
- Is thrilled to serve the Lord and share credit with others
- Rejoices when others are lifted up
- Is aware they cannot do the work of God (only He can & he is completely dependent on Him)
- Knows how much he needs to learn and is hungry for God
- Seeks God's face, not His hand
- Does not try to pretend
- Has no concern for self
- Compares self with God
- Knows that he can do nothing apart from God
- Spends time before God in the Word and prayer
- His heart breaks as he carries God's burdens

▸ **Exercise:**

In your own words, describe ministry done man's way: ____________________

____

____

In your own words, describe ministry done God's way: ____________________

____

____

"What shall we do that we can do the works God requires?"

Seeking to Know What God Requires of You

Ask yourself this question from the depths of your heart, as a person really seeking to find the answer: *"What shall we do that we may do the works God requires?"* Let this become a personal question. Let it become a real quest of your heart. Don't wait for a preacher or anyone else to tell you what God requires. You may come to the end of this study and nobody has told you, "This is exactly what God requires for you," but if you take it personally and you seek the Lord with your whole heart, He will begin to speak to you about what He requires of you.

Beloved, as time is growing late, God is going to do a new work in the nations. It may not come in the way we are dreaming or picturing. It may not start in the way we think it should. That's why we cannot afford to be complacent. We have to be seeking, crying out for God to reveal His heart and His purposes.

Jesus said that

- It has pleased the Father to reveal the mysteries of the Kingdom to the humble (Luke 10:21),
- "No one can come to me unless the Father who sent me draws him" (John 6:44), and
- "They will all be taught by God" (John 6:45).

So the cry of our hearts should be, "Lord, unless You draw me, I'm going to miss this move. I cannot get there by myself. I might not even recognize it when it starts, so Father join my heart to Yours. I lay down everything so that I can take hold of what You desire."

To summarize, in such an hour as this, when the nations look dark and hopeless, the Father is not asleep. He is at work. It pleases Him to reveal His heart, His work and mission, to those who seek Him, who give themselves to Him, and who surrender themselves to do His will and accomplish His good purpose.

Time for Reflection:

What is the most meaningful statement or scripture you read today? ____________________

What does God want you to do in response to this? ____________________

As you pray your prayer target for this day/week, what are you feeling the Holy Spirit is saying or calling you to and what is the warfare coming against you? ____________________

▸ Time for Prayer:

Take 1 hour to seek God. Continuing the prayer from yesterday, expect the Holy Spirit to lead you closer to the answer to this question: *"What must we do to do the work that God requires?"* Ask Him to begin to reveal the things that are hindering you from really "believing in the One He has sent" Begin to deal with this question and those below:

What is the Spirit revealing to you? ____________________

What is coming against you? ____________________

Lesson 3.
How Did Jesus Do the Work That God Required?

Testimony

Several years ago, God commissioned me and the ministry of World Trumpet Mission to go north, south, east, and west throughout Uganda to call the nation to repentance. Calling a nation to prayer and repentance is not a work a human or a ministry can do; it is a work that only God can do.

In obedience, we invited all the pastors in the nation to gather together so we could share the direction the Lord had given us, but very few responded. We sent letters to government officials and others in positions of authority in the nation to share the word the Lord had given us. Again, there was very little response.

I knew that God had a mission He wanted to do, but seeing that we weren't fulfilling that mission, I called the intercessors together, saying "We need to humble ourselves and seek God about why this work isn't going forward."

On the day that set to seek the Lord with the intercessors, during my morning prayer time, the Lord told me, "You can go to your meeting, but I will not go with you unless you surrender everything to Me." This perplexed me much! I thought – I knew – that I had already surrendered everything I could to God. As the day went along, I kept trying to put off what the Lord was asking of me, but I knew that He meant what He said: He would not go with me unless I surrendered everything.

I arrived a few hours early to spend some time in prayer before the meeting. As I was before the Lord, He showed me, "Surrender your family to me. No matter what takes place in your family, you must serve me." There were many other things the Lord showed me to surrender during that time; I spent the next 4 or 5 hours weeping and crying out while God showed me I needed to release my ministry, my reputation, my family; I need to release everything, no matter what happened or what cost I would have to pay.

On that day, I abandoned and surrendered everything that the Lord asked of me to the best of my ability. He went to the meeting very late and shared that I felt we needed to go into a very long fast, During the fast we would cry out to the Lord to open the nation, raise up prayer, and help repentance break forth. Within a week, the word had spread so quickly that almost 10,000 people around the nations had begun to join us in prayer and fasting. Within a short period of time after that, the President's office contacted us, pastors started to call and begin to gather, and the work began to spread into every sector of society.

> You cannot do the work of God; only He can do it through you.
>
> *—Pastor John Mulinde*

A few years later, we had a similar time of calling the nation to 14 days of repentance. Legislators, judiciaries, police officers, business leaders—people representing all sectors of society—came together, repenting for their sins and the sin of their nation. People from different districts repented for tribal issues. The President even handed the Ugandan flag to the intercessors and declared Uganda to be a Christian nation. The ministry saw God do a work we could have never done in our own power. Through these years of listening and obeying the word the Lord gave us, we learned a mighty lesson: you cannot do the work of God: only He can do it through you.

— Pastor John Mulinde

The Example Jesus Gave Us

Let us learn from Jesus Himself what it means to serve God. In the book of John, Jesus teaches us how He worked. He served the Father, doing only what He saw the Father doing (John 5:19) and saying only what the Father commanded Him to say (John 12:49-50). There are even two testimonies directly from the Father about Jesus' work: "That is my Son, whom I love; with him I am well pleased" (Matthew 3:17, 17:5). The Father did His work *through* His Son; Jesus did not do the work *for* Him. Even Jesus understood that. Jesus was abandoned to the Father, which made Him a vessel the Father could easily use.

How did Jesus serve God and do the works that He required? In John 5:17, Jesus says, *"My Father is always at his work to this very day, and I, too, am working."*

God is always at work. God is determined to finish His work, and He may invite you to become a part of that work. But you cannot *do* work for God; only God can work *through* you.

▶ **Exercise.**

Read John 5:19: "Jesus gave them this answer: 'I tell you the truth, the Son can do nothing by himself; he can do only what he sees his Father doing, because whatever the Father does the Son also does.'"

What can Jesus do by Himself ? ____________________________________

____

What does Jesus do? ____

____

Jesus is not just doing activity. He is deeply in tune with the Father's heart desires. He is on a mission to finish the work the Father has given Him to do. And He doesn't do the work in just any way; He only does what the Father tells Him and how the Father directs Him.

Jesus' heart was not to do just any ministry activity or good act. His heart burned to do His Father's will, to finish the work His Father gave Him to do.

▶ **Exercise:**

Look at Jesus' heart for God's work. In the scriptures below, circle key words that you notice about His heart.

- John 4:34: "My food," said Jesus, "is to do the will of him who sent me and to finish his work."
- John 6:38: "For I have come down from heaven not to do my will but to do the will of him who sent me."
- John 14:31: "But the world must learn that I love the Father and that I do exactly what my Father has commanded me."
- John 17:4: "I have brought you glory on earth by completing the work you gave me to do."

Mark the following statements as either true (T) or false (F):

____ I decide what I want to do to serve God.

____ God does the work through me; I cannot do His work.

____ God has a mission He is seeking to accomplish in this generation.

____ I need to seek God and get His heart, then align myself to His mission.

Jesus' heart was not to do just any ministry activity or good act. His heart burned to do His Father's will, to finish the work His Father gave Him to do.

God Will Reveal His Work to Us

▶ **Exercise:**

Read John 5:20: "For the Father loves the Son and shows him all he does. Yes, to your amazement he will show him even greater things than these." How does the Father respond to the kind of heart Jesus had? ___________

____

____

Jesus said, "As the Father has loved me, so have I loved you" (John 15:9). If the Father loved Jesus that way, Jesus loves us in the same way. **He will reveal His work to those who seek Him.** It pleases His heart to reveal His work to us; to pass the Father's heart desires on to us; and to give us the authority, ability, and power to do what He wants to do.

God is at work. And in these days, when the time is growing short, the Lord is not just sitting down watching. He is **at work**. He has a mission. He has goals He wants to accomplish. Are we willing to give Him our lives for Him to work through us?

Time for Reflection:

What is the most meaningful statement or scripture you read today? ___________

What does God want you to do in response to this? ___________

As you pray your prayer target for this day/week, what are you feeling the Holy Spirit is saying or calling you to and what is the warfare coming against you? ___________

▸ **Time for Prayer:**

- Does your heart burn for God's heart?
- For His mission?

If not, what is hindering you from joining Him in His mission? Ask the Lord to search your heart. Humbly open yourself up to the Holy Spirit, allowing Him to reveal to you anything that would keep you from pursuing God's desires and fulfilling His mission. Journal what the Holy Spirit shows you below. ______________________________

Lesson 4.
How Do We Do Ministry and Not Just Good Works?

The Bible says that the work that God requires, the work of ministry, is not simply the good acts that people do (Matthew 7:21-23): preaching the gospel, feeding the poor, clothing the naked, building schools and hospitals, etc. Those acts in themselves are ministry; they could be works or activities that God requires. However, simply doing those things that we normally think of as "ministry" may not constitute what God thinks of as "ministry."

Not everyone who says to me, "Lord, Lord," will enter the kingdom of heaven, but only he who does the will of my Father who is in heaven. Many will say to me on that day, "Lord, Lord, did we not prophesy in your name, and in your name drive out demons and perform many miracles?" Then I will tell them plainly, "I never knew you. Away from me, you evildoers!"
Matthew 7:21-23

Jesus said, "Not everyone who says to me, 'Lord, Lord,' will enter the kingdom of heaven, but only he who does the will of my Father who is in heaven." In other words, they will come on that Day, saying "Master! We prophesied in Your name. We worked miracles in Your name. We preached in Your name." Are those the works of ministry? We think so, but Jesus will say, "Get out of my sight, you workers of iniquity."

What Is "Ministry"?

Ministry is not simply doing good activities. Ministry is doing what the heart of God desires. Jesus calls it "the will of God." A key question we need to resolve by the end of this study is "What is God requiring in this day and time?"

When you ponder such a question, you realize that God has desired different things at different times in history:

- For man to rule Creation
- For Israel to reveal Him to the nations of the world
- For the church to disciple the nations

However, all those things point toward one eternal purpose of God: that He would be glorified; that all He is and has within Him would be revealed to the world.

God's Work in Noah's Generation

There was a time when God purposed to destroy the whole world. Why? The whole world had become defiled and corrupted because of the wickedness of man. Creation had lost its ability to glorify God; to reveal all

> God blessed them and said to them, "Be fruitful and increase in number; fill the earth and subdue it. Rule over the fish of the sea and the birds of the air and over every living creature that moves on the ground."
> Genesis 1:28

that He is and has within Him. God analyzed the situation and decided to destroy everything and start over again. In other words, His heart's desire was to cleanse the world and make a new beginning. God came to the one man, Noah, who found favor in His eyes, and said, "Build Me an ark." **He invited Noah to join Him in His work.**

▶ **Exercise:**

Read Genesis 6:5-22. Stop a moment and ask, "What is ministry?" If we based our answer on the story of Noah and said, "Ministry is building an ark for the Lord," we would be far from the truth. Noah fulfilled God's mission and the desire of His heart by building an ark. If we did that today, though, we would be thousands of miles away from God's mission and heart's desire.

Noah building an ark and taking care of the animals was ministry. Why? Because it was in line with what God wanted to accomplish at the time; it enabled God to cleanse the world and make a new beginning.

Define "ministry" as you have known it to be in your own life and in the church: ____

____

____

How does God define "ministry"? ____

____

____

Noah did everything the Lord commanded him, which fulfilled the desire's of God's heart. This was the ministry that God had called Noah to do. Noah's complete obedience and trust in the Lord fulfilled the purposes of God in his day and time. *That is ministry!*

> Then God blessed Noah and his sons, saying to them, "Be fruitful and increase in number and fill the earth."
> Genesis 9:1

When God came to make a covenant with Noah, He gave him exactly the same commission He had given Adam. What Adam failed to do is the exact thing the Lord gave to Noah to do, using the exact same words. Then God began to work with Noah until Noah's failure also became evident. The failures that both Adam and Noah experienced came when they decided to do things their way rather than God's way.

God's Mission Through Abraham

After the time of the flood God saw that, still, "every inclination of man's heart is evil" (Genesis 8:21). The Lord was forced to scatter the people over the face of the earth because they preferred to settle and build a city and tower at Babel rather than fulfill His heart's desire for them to "be fruitful and increase in number and fill the earth" (Genesis 9:1). To fulfill His desire for a people who would be His and glorify Him, He decided to make a nation for Himself through Abram: "The Lord had said to Abram, 'Leave your country, your people and your father's household and go to the land I will show you. I will make you into a great nation and I will bless you; I will make your name great, and you will be a blessing. I will bless those who bless you, and whoever curses you I will curse; and all peoples on earth will be blessed through you" (Genesis 12:1-3).

God had a mission He wanted to accomplish through Abraham. He said, "All nations are not My nations. I'm going to take a man and make a nation out of him. Those will be My people. I will be their God." He had a purpose: to build a nation of people He could redeem, a people He could draw out of darkness, so that through this nation, He would be revealed to the nations of the world.

Lot Stepped Away From God's Mission

There are people we read about in the Bible who made what we would consider small mistakes in human reasoning, but God's judgments were so severe on them. One example is when Lot separated from Abram. Abram said, "If you go to the left, I'll go to the right" (Genesis 13:9). Soon after Lot chose to leave, God came to Abram, reminded him of His promises and covenant with him, and showed Abram He had nothing to do with Lot's choice to leave (Genesis 13:14-18).

Read Genesis 13:8-20. When Sodom and Gomorrah were attacked, God did not warn Lot. He allowed him to be taken into captivity. After Abram pursued and defeated the attackers, Melchizedek tells us that it was the Lord who gave Abram the victory (v 20). Why did God give Abram the victory when He could have warned Lot what was about to happen?

This isn't just about understanding the heart of God. It is about joining God where He is at work. Lot had separated himself from the work God was doing through Abraham. When God came to judge Sodom and Gomorrah, He didn't warn Lot, who was in Sodom. He went to Abraham, saying, "Can I do anything without telling Abraham, My friend?" (Genesis 18:17-19).

When we step away from God's heart desire, we can no longer be productive.

What was God doing? To paraphrase, God was saying, "I want to make a nation out of one man, and anybody who associates with that man and his household and circumcises his males after My covenant, those I will work with. That is My heart. Why? Because I want to raise a nation through whom I will reveal Myself to the nations of the world, until I can redeem the nations back to Myself."

Lot stepped away from God's mission, and God was not going to produce a second nation out of him. God's heart was to produce a nation out of Abraham. Mistakes may look small, but once a person goes against the desires of God's heart, God can do nothing through him until he repents.

▶ **Exercise:**

Why must we understand the heart of God? ______________________________

____

____

When we step away from God's heart desire, we can no long be productive, and we will not see God beginning to use us or work through us until we repent and come back to His heart's desire.

Time for Reflection:

What is the most meaningful statement or scripture you read today? ______________________________

What does God want you to do in response to this? ______________________________

As you pray your prayer target for this day/week, what are you feeling the Holy Spirit is saying or calling you to and what is the warfare coming against you? ______________________________

▸ **Time for Prayer:**

You are taking this study because you desire to be used by God, and because you have a heart to seek after Him and to see His purposes go forth in your heart, your home, your community and perhaps your nation. In humility and contrition, ask God to show you the difference between doing good works and doing ministry, fulfilling the heart of the Father. Continue to seek Him to take you from where you are to where He wants you to be.

Notes

Week 3.

God Is At Work

> **GOAL OF THE WEEK:**
>
> As we go through this week's lessons, we will begin to
> 1. Have a clearer understanding of how God works, what His heart's desire is, what He is doing in our day and time, and how we can join Him in His work.
> 2. Have greater insight into how we can work the works that God requires.

We started our study by asking, "What shall we do to do the works that God requires?" To recognize what the works of God are, we must first understand His heart.

Understanding the desires of God's heart is the only way we can confidently know we are doing the work of God. We know He is at work. He is always at work (John 5:17), and we have learned that He will invite us to take part in that work. However, if we don't clearly understand that He has specific purposes and objectives and join Him in those, all our energy, time, and effort will be spent on just another program, another strategy, or another activity. The labor we invest in serving the Lord will have been wasted and produce little fruit.

This is happening all around us, including inside the church. Today's church is unable to fulfill its earthly mandate. Much of the time, the work we are doing is not fulfilling the desires of God's heart. This is not meant to condemn the church; it is a wake-up call.

> **Prayer targets for week 3:**
>
> 1. To connect with God's work through the eras and begin to seek His heart.
> 2. To connect with His heart's desires in our present era.

Is the church raising up people who have radically devoted themselves to Christ? Are they pushing back the darkness in our communities and seeing the kingdom of God being established? Or are we seeing people just attending services? Is the church fulfilling the mission Christ gave us 2,000 years ago?

We need to ask these types of questions because if the church, like individuals, breaks away from communion and dependency on God, it will be rendered ineffective from being a true vessel through which God can work.

> **Audio/video link for week 3:**
>
> 
>
> http://worldtrumpet.org/awakening-the-church (week 3)

Lesson 1.
Knowing the Heart of God

Six Eras in the Bible

- Creation
- Establishing Nations
- Raising Up Israel
- Sending the Messiah, Jesus Christ
- Raising up the Church
- The Day of the Lord

The scriptures clearly show us the desires of God's heart and the work that He is doing. They reveal the purposes and goals He has in mind, and give us insight and understanding into what He is trying to accomplish at certain times in history. A close study of the Bible reveals eras in which God has worked, is working, and which He is planning to bring about. Understanding each of these eras gives us insight into God's heart, and helps us clearly know what He is trying to accomplish and how we can join Him in that work.

To help us grasp God's intentions in our day and time, we will review each of these eras. As we do, we will come to see several truths:

1. God's heart desires do not change; He continues to have the same goals and purposes throughout time.
2. If God rejected something at one time in history, He will continue to reject that thing in all other eras, including our own. For example, God rejected the nations – and Israel – because they turned to idolatry, just as He would the church today.
3. Just doing religious rituals and routines, and not fulfilling God's heart—like Israel—will not satisfy God, as it never has in any other time. God told Israel he was tired of their meaningless offerings and assemblies, and that He was not satisfied with their fasts (see Isaiah chapters 1 & 58).

The heavens declare the glory of God; the skies proclaim the work of his hands.
Psalm 19:1

As we go through this week's lessons, we will also begin to come to a clearer understanding of how God works, what His heart's desire is, what He is doing in our day and time, and how we can join Him in His work. We will have greater insight into how we can work the works that God requires. We will begin by studying the first era: the creation of the world.

Era 1 — Creation

"In the beginning God created the heavens and the earth" (Genesis 1:1). Why?

In Genesis 1:1-25, we see God creating the universe. He made the sun and moon, the stars and sky, the day and night, the earth and sea, and all the plants and animals that dwell on the earth. He paused at the end of each day and analyzed what He had made. The Scriptures say several times, "And God saw that it was good" (vv 6, 9, 12, 18, 21, 25). His heart was pleased. The things He desired were being fulfilled.

> Who among the gods is like you, O Lord? Who is like you—majestic is holiness, awesome in glory, working wonders?
> Exodus 15:10-12

The Glory of God Revealed Through Creation. In the beginning, God was revealing Himself by bringing forth a creation that would reflect His nature, glory, and character; even His very image in the creation of man. The first mission God set for Himself was, through creation, to reveal the mystery of who He is, to demonstrate who He is and what is inside Him. Everything He created had the ability to bless all other parts of creation, and as every created thing shared its blessing with the rest, the joy and the love of God would be shared among all creation. Creation would truly reflect the glory of God.

If we step back to look at this early stage of God's work, we see His desire to reveal Himself through creation and that He was very pleased with what He had done.

Man Created to Rule. By Genesis 1:25, God had created all the animals; in verse 26, He said, "Let us make man in our image, in our likeness, and let them rule over... all the creatures."

> You are worthy, our Lord and God, to receive glory and honor and power, for you created all things, and by your will they were created and have their being.
> Revelation 4:10-11

▶ **Exercise:**

God could have stopped after He created all the plants and animals and simply allowed them to exist. Instead, it was His heart's desire to make man. Why? ____________________

____

God wanted a people to steward creation and make sure it fulfilled God's desired purpose. He wanted man to walk in communion with Him and to shepherd His creation. He wanted man to rule.

> "Jesus called them together and said, "You know that the rulers of the Gentiles lord it over them, and their high officials exercise authority over them. Not so with you. Instead, whoever wants to become great among you must be your servant, and whoever wants to be first must be your slave— just as the Son of Man did not come to be served, but to serve, and to give his life as a ransom for many."
> Matthew 20:25-30

A Deeper Look at God's Heart Desires

In Matthew 20:25-26, Jesus told the disciples that the rulers of the world lord it over their subjects, but not so in the Kingdom of God. He said, "Instead, whoever wants to become great among you must become your servant." Therefore, when we read, "Let us make man to rule," we need to understand ruling the way that God does, not the way the world does. We have to think of ruling as serving, and serving as shepherding.

▶ **Exercise:**

Read Matthew 20:25-30. From scripture and your own experience, what is the world's way of ruling? ____________________

____

____

What is God's way? ____________________

____

____

Provide an example of God's way of ruling: ____________________

____

____

It pleased God's heart to have one creature preside over the rest. God wanted man to shepherd, or rule, His creation. He created man to preside over all other creatures and to steward them so they could bring forth the purpose for which they were created.

The Ministry of Man. In last week's study, we said that ministry is not activities; it is fulfilling the desire of God's heart.

▶ **Exercise:**

What was God's heart desire in this first era of Creation? ____________________

____

____

In the beginning, the desire of God's heart was that every creature would reveal His glory and that God would be known among and through His creation. God chose to do this by having man preside and "rule" over all creation.

The true ministry of man is to do what God desires. When we do that, we reflect His glory.

When God created man, He did two very important things. First, He created man in His own image and likeness. That means something of man was like God. He possessed the nature and likeness of God. Why? Because God wanted there to be deep communion between man and God, which would allow man to tap into the infinite knowledge of God. This included the purposes and desires of God's heart.

Second, after God created man in His own image and likeness, He blew into him the breath of life. Something came from inside God to the inside of man, making it possible for something deep in man to call upon the deep in God. God blew His very life and essence into man (Genesis 2:7).

Man's Communion With God. Genesis 2:19-20 says, "Now the Lord God had formed out of the ground all the beasts of the field and all the birds of the air. He brought them to the man to see what he would name them; and whatever the man called each living creature, that was its name. So the man gave names to all the livestock, the birds of the air, and all the beasts of the field." How was this so? Adam was being led by the Spirit of God; by the deep communion and spiritual connection between them. Deep was calling unto deep (Psalm 42:7).

▶ **Exercise:**

What was the secret behind Adam's ability to name all the living creatures? ____

____

____

Adam's heart was in connection and communion with the heart of God. The breath of God was inside him, revealing everything to him. So what is our secret today? It's that same place of dependency, trust, and reliance upon Him. That place of abiding. This is also the secret of the power, authority, knowledge, and the ability of all mankind to do the ministry that God calls us to do. (We will refer to this later as "covenant position.")

An essential key to our doing the work of God is our communion and dependency upon Him.

To help Adam remain in a state of deep communion with Him, God warned him, "You are free to eat from any tree in the garden; but you must not eat from the tree of the knowledge of good and evil, for when you eat of it you will surely die" (Genesis 2:16-17).

▶ **Exercise:**

What was God's intention in those instructions? What was He saying to the man? ____

____

____

God was trying to tell Adam to not live by his own understanding, to not judge things with his own judgment, and – most importantly – to not break the fellowship and communion he had with God. In other words, God was saying, "Adam, your power, your strength, and your life all come by staying in communion with Me."

Brothers and sisters, what shall we do that we may work the works of God?

The deeper the dependency, the more useful the vessel becomes in God's hands. This is a foundational stone in seeing God beginning to do His work through us. It is not us doing work *for Him*; it is Him doing work *through us*. There is no limit to what God can do through a vessel that is yielded and completely dependant on Him.

You can see that while Adam was walking in communion with God, he was fulfilling the heart desires of God and the work of God was being accomplished. However, once this communion was broken, Adam was no longer living in dependency on God and therefore was unable to do the work that God required of him. We should never permit our hearts to stray from dependency, but always long for our dependency to deepen as we go forward with God and allow Him to work through us.

▸ **Pause to Pray and Seek the Lord:**

We can often feel the pressures, doubts, fears, and other pulls of the world that want to push us, squeeze us, and tighten our hearts; these can cause us to take back some of our trust and to turn back to self-reliance and self-dependency. We must constantly and daily spend time in prayer to push these things back and come to a place where we're expanding the abandonment of our hearts and broadening the trust of our spirit to rely on the indwelling Christ.

If the key to doing the work of God – to connecting with His heart and beginning to walk in His power – is staying in dependency and communion with Him, then it is crucial that we are constantly in prayer. We must push back those things that want to close us down and pull us back into self-trust and self-reliance; those things that cause us – like Eve – to doubt that God is trustworthy, that He is capable, that we can give all our trust to Him, and that He will do the work.

Spend the next 15 to 30 minutes with the Lord. Humble yourself and ask God to reveal any way you have turned from full dependency upon Him and anything you have taken back into your own hands, your own mind, your own strength, or your own will. Ask Him to undo these things and bring you to a deeper place of dependency on Him. Journal anything you begin to see in yourself, and cry out for Him to lead you to the place of total surrender and trust in Him. Then, thank Him and trust Him for doing a work that only He can do. ________________________________

____

____

____

____

____

____

____

____

____

____

____

____

____

"The world has yet to see what God can do with a man fully consecrated to Him. By God's help, I aim to be that man."

—quote popularized by D.L. Moody (originally quoted by British revivalist Henry Varley)

> Now the serpent was craftier than any of the wild animals the Lord God had made. He said to the woman, "Did God really say, 'You must not eat from any tree in the garden'?" The woman replied to the serpent, "We may eat fruit from the trees in the garden, but God did say, 'You must not eat fruit from the tree that is in the middle of the garden, and you must not touch it, or you will die.'" "You will not surely die," the serpent said to the woman. "For God knows that when you eat of it your eyes will be opened, and you will be like God, knowing good and evil. When the woman saw that the fruit of the tree was good for food and pleasing to the eye, and also desirable for gaining wisdom, she took some and ate it. She also gave some to her husband, who was with her, and he ate it."
>
> Genesis 3:1-7

The Fall of Man. Adam was given a clear mandate, and he learned that he could do the work God required of him by staying dependent on God. But the devil, who comes to steal, kill, and destroy (John 10:10), knows that the secret of man's life is found in his communion with God. Paul wrote to the Corinthians, "I am afraid that just as Eve was deceived by the serpent's cunning, your minds may somehow be led astray from your sincere and pure devotion to Christ" (2 Corinthians 11:3). Paul knew we needed that deep devotion that brings communion, and that the serpent would try to destroy it.

▸ **Exercise:**

Read the dialogue between the serpent and Eve in Genesis 3:1-7.

How did the serpent lie to Eve? ______________________

____

____

How did Eve come into agreement with these lies? ______________

____

____

What was the consequence of Eve believing the serpent's lies? ________

____

____

The devil told Eve that she would no longer have to depend on God or be led by Him. Like God, she would be able to make her own decisions and do whatever she wanted. So she and Adam disobeyed God's instructions and ate some of the forbidden fruit. And Eve agreed with the serpent. The Bible says she saw that the fruit of the tree was good for food, pleasing to the eye, and desirable to bring wisdom.

> Then, after desire has conceived, it gives birth to sin; and sin, when it is full-grown, gives birth to death.
>
> James 1:15

Once she believed the serpent's lies, Eve was no longer certain that God was faithful and that she could fully trust Him. Her actions broke the trust and dependency she and her husband had in God and they could no longer surrender themselves fully to Him.

As was said earlier, we need to restore the communion and dependency on God that was lost when man fell. The first man, Adam, lost this communion. Dependency was broken, trust had faded, faith was weakened, and surrender was gone. Man fell and was now walking according to his own wisdom and not the wisdom of God.

Time for Reflection:

What do we learn from this era? What does God reject? What does He require? ______________________________

What does God want you to do in response to this? ______________________________

As you pray your prayer target for this day/week, what are you feeling the Holy Spirit is saying or calling you to and what is the warfare coming against you? ______________________________

▸ Time for Prayer:

Allow the Lord to examine your heart and to reveal anything within that hinders deep communion with Him. Ask Him to change your heart so that you are able to give yourself to Him in full abandonment and full trust. As you see things that stand in the way, such as doubt or fear—any form of resistance to God and His ways—humble yourself before Him and allow Him to deal with these things in your heart.

Lesson 2.
God Continues to Fulfill His Purposes

The purposes of God do not change. He is the same yesterday, today, and tomorrow. And even if those He has called out to join Him in His work fail and turn away, He has continued throughout history to stay focused on His goals and plans.

The scriptures show that after the creation, when man fell and turned away from the purposes of God, a second era began, which we will call "Establishing Nations." As we study this era, you will see that God continues to be about His work of redeeming mankind and bringing them into His purposes.

Era 2— Establishing Nations

Man to Fill and Rule the Earth. The scriptures show that early on, man began to disobey the mandate and instructions the Lord gave him. After the fall of man, the broken communion with God made it easy for man to rebel and resist God's commands, and man began to make decisions based on his own desires and wisdom.

In Genesis, God told Adam and Eve (Genesis 1:28) , and then Noah and his sons (Genesis 9:1-2), to increase in number and fill the whole earth, and to rule over creation. This was the mandate that God gave to all mankind.

This was still the desire of God's heart. He wanted man to spread out all over the earth and rule over creation. We can see in Genesis 10:32 that man began with good intentions – they started out by following these instructions – but just a few verses later, things start to change.

> These are the clans of Noah's sons, according to their lines of descent, within their nations. From these the nations spread out over the earth after the flood.
> Genesis 10:32

▶ **Exercise:**

Read Genesis 11:1-9 and answer the following questions:

What was man choosing to do? ______________________________

____

____

How did this go against the desires of God's heart? ____________________

____

____

What was God's response to these actions? ____________________

____

____

Man decided to settle in one land. They chose to make a name for themselves so they would not be scattered over the face of the earth. They went against the desires of God and began to fulfill the desires of their own hearts. They abandoned His instructions to fill the earth and rule creation.

God responded by confusing their language and scattering them over the whole earth. He forced them to do His will and to fill the earth, something they had wanted to resist. God is faithful to His plans and had not given up on His purposes or His heart's desires. He was working to fulfill His desire that man would fill the earth and rule over all creation.

The Creation of Nations. The word "nation" first appears in the Bible in Genesis 10. It comes out of the genealogies of the three sons of Noah. Out of the forced scattering at Babel, small groups of people found a territory where they could settle and began to grow, first as communities and then eventually into nations.

> From one man he made every nation of men, that they should inhabit the whole earth; and he determined the times set for them and the exact places where they should live. God did this so that men would seek him and perhaps reach out for him and find him, though he is not far from each one of us.
>
> Acts 17:26-27

Acts 17:26 says that God determined the times and exact places where man and nations should live. In addition, Deuteronomy 32:8 says, "When the Most High gave the nations their inheritance, when he divided all mankind, he set up boundaries for the peoples." So we see in this judgment of Babel that God was still in control. He was still working to fulfill His desire to establish nations.

The people did not go wherever they wanted. God was the one who determined their territories. He established the boundaries for each person and each nation; therefore, He is the author of the nations. What is interesting is that to human reasoning it looked like things had gone very wrong. The people were scattered over the whole earth, which is not the way they wanted it. But our God is a wonderful God. Even in the act of scattering, He deposited redemptive purposes within every person and nation. Acts 17:27 says, "God did this so that men would seek him and perhaps reach out for him and find Him, though he is not far from each one of us." Even in this act of judgment, God was working His plan of redemption. Praise the Lord!

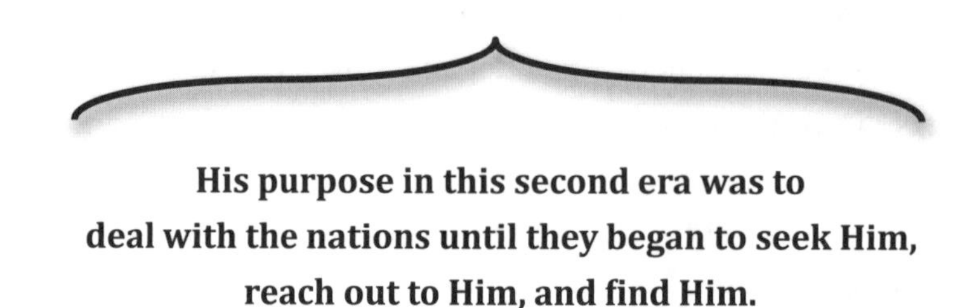

His purpose in this second era was to deal with the nations until they began to seek Him, reach out to Him, and find Him.

From the point of scattering we see God addressing and judging the nations – the Amorites, Cushites, Egyptians, Assyrians, etc. God is no longer dealing with man as an individual. He is dealing with men as corporate societies, as nations.

Elements of Society. Nations are made up of societies, and God gave us five basic elements that build a society. These are:

1. Government
2. Worship
3. Family
4. Economic systems
5. Belief systems

Government. God created man to rule, so government is part of God's plan. Government is the administration of the society that God has given to man, and was intended to help man accomplish his mandate to rule, steward, and shepherd creation to help it fulfill God's purposes.

Worship. God created man to worship and commune with Him. His desire was that man would worship the one true living God, and love Him more than anything.

Family. God made woman for man and established the concept of family. "For this cause a man will leave his father and mother, and be united to his wife, and they will become one flesh" (Genesis 2:24). They were to reproduce and teach their children the ways of God. The family was the building block of the nations.

Economic system. God made all creation to have the potential to multiply and bring forth more value. He told the man to subdue, have dominion, and multiply. As wealth was produced, man was to use it to minister and care for one another. A study of Deuteronomy 8:1-18 illustrates the blessings and wealth that God intends to give His people. The scripture also warns us to "remember the Lord your God, for it is He who gives you the ability to produce wealth."

Belief system. God gave man instructions, commands, and eventually the Law as a blueprint for a belief system based on His wisdom. These instructions, laws, decrees, and commands ensure man's protection, security, provision, power, authority, and communion with God.

Corruption of Nations. Because the nations were established on human and worldly wisdom, and not on God's wisdom or ways, the elements of society became and continue to be corrupted. Creation was not operating according to God's will. The ways the people lived and what they worshiped drew the darkness and made them captives to the enemy. They had become slaves of the darkness they were drawing. The nations had strayed away from the wisdom and way of God, and instead of these elements of society being the blessing and protection God intended them to be, they had now become sources of bondage and destruction.

> For although they knew God, they neither glorified him as God nor gave thanks to him, but their thinking became futile and their foolish hearts were darkened. Although they claimed to be wise, they became fools and exchanged the glory of the immortal God for images made to look like mortal man and birds and animals and reptiles.
>
> Romans 1:21-23

▸ **Exercise:**

Pick three of the five elements of society. List ways they have fallen from God's ways and wisdom and, instead of being a blessing and protection to society, how they are defiling and holding it captive.

Element #1: ______________ List: ______________________________

____

____

Element #2: ______________ List: ______________________________

____

____

Element #3: ______________ List: ______________________________

____

____

The nations had become corrupted and that corruption continues even today. For example, man was created to worship, so we will worship something. But because we have strayed so far from the heart of God, we have begun to worship created things, ourselves, sports, hobbies, etc. We were created to love God with all of our heart, to worship Him. He is the source of all of life to us, but we have come to the place where we worship things made by man.

We can also see how the concept of family has become so confused and disoriented. People don't know the purpose of family, what their role is, how to act toward one another, how to parent, etc. Many don't even know what "family" means or how to hold up the values God has placed on it.

Moving Into the Next Era

When God looked at the earth and the nations that were forming, He once again saw people and creation locked up in prisons of corruption and evil desires. Every aspect of society – government, worship, family, economic system, and belief system – had become corrupt because man was living in his fallen state and trusting in his human wisdom rather than the wisdom of God. The nations did not even have a clear understanding of who their Creator or their God was. They would bow down and worship Creation or idols they had created with their own hands. They had lost perspective of the truth. They were getting more and more corrupt and further and further from His heart's desires.

God saw that the nations had become corrupt and were far away from His intention and desire that they would worship and follow Him, so He moved into the next era: to create a nation through which He could reveal Himself to all the other nations of the world and draw them back to Himself.

Time for Reflection:

What do we learn from this era? What does God reject? What does He require? ________________________________

What does God want you to do in response to this? ________________________________

As you pray your prayer target for this day/week, what are you feeling the Holy Spirit is saying or calling you to and what is the warfare coming against you? ________________________________

▸ **Time for Prayer:**

The Lord asks us to remove the idols from our hearts, anything that corrupts our relationship with Him. Spend time before Him today asking Him to reveal any idols in your heart, then lay them before Him. Spend time in confession and repentance, and ask Him to set you free of the influence and impact they have had on your life.

Now the earth was corrupt in God's sight and was full of violence. God saw how corrupt the earth had become, for all the people on earth had corrupted their ways.
Genesis 6:11-12

Lesson 3.

God Creates a Nation for His Purposes

In the last few lessons, we learned that the entire world was liable for destruction and that God would have been totally justified if He had destroyed all of creation and started over (Genesis 6:5-7). But instead, He moved into a new era with a new mission: He was going to raise up a nation through which He would reveal Himself to the nations of the world and prove that there is no other God besides Himself (Exodus 6:6-8,34:10-14). He would reveal His power, authority, and sovereignty through this nation, and the world would then see that there is no other god like the God of Israel (Deuteronomy 4:32-40, Ezekiel 36:22-23, Daniel 6:25-27).

Instead of destruction, our merciful God determined in His heart that He was going to work a plan of redemption until He had brought the nations back to Himself and His purposes (Genesis 8:20-21).

Era 3— Raising up Israel

As you read the Bible, you see that the nations began to stray; they began to turn away from God. Instead of worshiping their creator, they began to worship created things, and then wickedness began to draw closer in all its forms. The idolatry, the depraved minds, the immorality, the selfishness – all of this became rampant in the nations.

▶ Exercise:

Read the following scriptures and answer the question, "How did the nations stray away from God?"

Deuteronomy 18:9-12: ____________________

____

Deuteronomy 9:4-5: ____________________

____

Deuteronomy 12:29-31: ____________________

____

Deuteronomy 4:15-19: ____________________

____

Numbers 25:1-3: ____________________

____

The scriptures say that God found the practices of the nations detestable. They worshiped and built altars to false gods and things that God had created, they were involved in divination, sorcery, and witchcraft, and consulted the dead. They even burned their children as sacrifices to there false gods. The Lord said that it was on account of their own wickedness that the Lord was driving the nations out from the land that He was giving to Israel.

God rejected the nations and the way that they had begun to function, and He began the next era, raising up a nation through which He could reveal who He was: Creator, Sovereign King, Name Above All Names, and so much more. He wanted the nations to witness His wisdom, His power, and His glory, and to draw them back into communion and dependency upon Him.

God's Purpose for Israel. God's heart desire is to redeem the nations, to restore all creation back to Himself. Therefore, after the decline of the nations, God looked at the situation and began this era.

God's heart's desire was to raise up one nation whose testimony would have an impact on all the other nations on the earth; a nation that would bless every other nation.

God birthed the nation of Israel and then purposed to set it apart from the nations of the world and draw it to Himself. He said, "This nation will be My inheritance. It will have My name and be My nation. I will bless it and pour into it. Through this nation, I will reveal to every other nation on the earth that I am the one true God (Genesis 12:2-3, Exodus 8:22-23)." God wanted the nations to see that their idols, the things that they coveted and desired, were nothing like the God of Israel. He wanted to reveal His power, glory, ways, and instructions through Israel, and use them to show the rest of the world the way that He wanted them to live; the way they could have life and have it to the fullest, with Him as their God. Through Israel, He would draw the nations back to Himself (Leviticus 22:31-33, Deuteronomy 4:5-8, Isaiah 12:4,44:6-23, Romans 16:26).

God's Relationship With Israel. God planned to show His power and glory to all the other nations on the earth by dwelling with Israel; they would be His people and He would be their God. And that is what He did. God's presence was literally with Israel.

▶ **Exercise:**

Read the following scriptures. Describe God's interaction with His people.

Genesis 15:1-5: ______________________________

____

____

Genesis 17:1-9: ______________________________

____

____

Exodus 13:21-22: ______________________________

____

____

Exodus 15:6-16: ______________________________

____

____

Exodus 33:7-11: ______________________________

____

____

Deuteronomy 5:7-22: ______________________________

____

____

God called out Abram and commissioned him to be the "Father of nations," telling him that his descendants would number more than the stars in the sky. He made a covenant with Abram that He promised would be everlasting. As He delivered them from Egypt and every enemy that they faced, God walked with them, dwelled among them, gave them His law, and communed face to face with Moses. He reestablished the communion and dependency of the people on Himself as He led Israel through the wilderness with a cloud by day and a pillar of fire by night, and performed great wonders and miracles that made all the nations tremble as they witnessed His power.

God was actively involved with Israel in every situation. He led them and protected them. Their shoes never wore out as they wandered in the desert 40 years (Deuteronomy 29:2-8). If they needed water, He brought it from a rock (Exodus 17:5-6). Even as they came into the Promised Land, He gave them victory after victory. They had no foes they could not defeat. God walked with Israel and fulfilled His covenant with them (Joshua 10:40-42,23:3-5,9-10,14). He even told them, "I am even going to be roaming in the camp as you are sleeping in the night (Deuteronomy 23:14)." He demonstrated His glory through them and provided for them in powerful and wonderful ways.

Exodus 15:14-16:

- The nations will hear and tremble
- anguish will grip the people of Philistia
- the leaders of Moab will be seized with trembling
- the people of Canaan will melt away
- terror and dread will fall upon them
- by the power of your arm they will be as still as stone

▶ Exercise:

Read Deuteronomy 2:24-32 (below). Circle the instructions that God gave Moses and the Israelites. Draw a box around the promises and His presence that He poured out on them.

> "Set out now and cross the Arnon Gorge. See, I have given into your hand Sihon the Amorite, king of Heshbon, and his country. Begin to take possession of it and engage him in battle. This very day I will begin to put the terror and fear of you on all the nations under heaven. They will hear reports of you and will tremble and be in anguish because of you."
>
> From the desert of Kedemoth I [Moses] sent messengers to Sihon king of Heshbon offering peace and saying, "Let us pass through your country. We will stay on the main road; we will not turn aside to the right or to the left. Sell us food to eat and water to drink for their price in silver. Only let us pass through on foot—as the descendants of Esau, who live in Seir, and the Moabites, who live in Ar, did for us—until we cross the Jordan into the land the Lord our God is giving us." But Sihon king of Heshbon refused to let us pass through. For the Lord your God had made his spirit stubborn and his heart obstinate in order to give him into your hands, as he has now done.
>
> The Lord said to me, "See, I have begun to deliver Sihon and his country over to you. Now begin to conquer and possess his land."
>
> When Sihon and all his army came out to meet us in battle at Jahaz, the Lord our God delivered him over to us and we struck him down, together with his sons and his whole army.

> "This very day I will begin to put the terror and fear of you on all the nations under heaven. They will hear reports of you and will tremble and be in anguish because of you."
> Deuteronomy 2:25

The nations trembled when they saw Israel and the power of its God. Even the superpowers of the day knew without a doubt that Israel's God was with them. He established Himself as the One above everything. There was no other god like Him.

To be the nation through which God could reveal Himself, it was also required that Israel be different from all the other nations. God told them, "You cannot become like the nations around you. You cannot worship their gods, you cannot do the things that they do, you cannot intermarry with them, you cannot observe their customs. You must be surrendered and set apart unto me (Leviticus 20:22-26). If you go against My ways or My will, you will begin to lose the very purpose for which I created you (Deuteronomy 28:15-68,30:11-19, Joshua 24:19-20). I called you out so that you could be a witness to all the nations, so I could manifest myself through you; this will draw you out of the darkness, out of the wickedness, out of the destruction, and the nations will begin to realize that there is no god like the God of Israel. And as you do this – as you obey my commands and decrees – I will be your God and you will by my people. I will defend you and provide for you. I will be your security and strength. There is nothing you need that I will not provide" (Deuteronomy 28:1-14,29:9, Exodus 19:5-6).

When Israel turns away from the ways of God,
they lose the very purpose for which they were created.

> "Now if you obey me fully and keep my covenant, then out of all nations you will be my treasured possession. Although the whole earth is mine, you will be for me a kingdom of priests and a holy nation."
> Exodus 19:5-6

Israel Strays From the Purposes of God. Every time Israel began to lose sight of these commands and instructions, they started to desire to be like the other nations. Instead of God being their King, they wanted a king like all the other nations. They started wanting to go the way of the nations, to do things the way the nations did. The nations started to affect Israel rather than Israel having an effect on the nations.

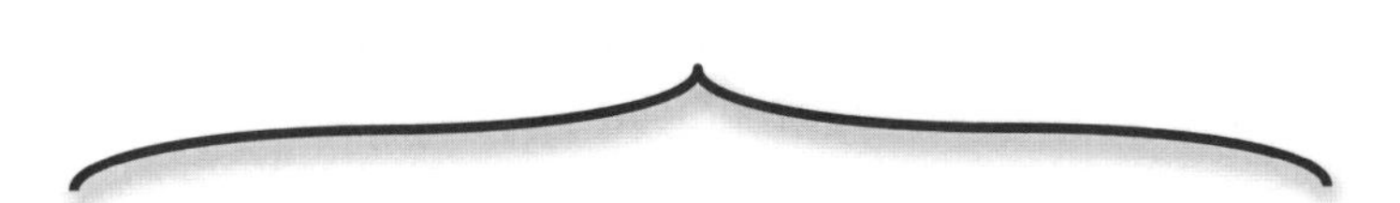

Israel was supposed to be the vehicle through which God would reveal Himself, but then they started to become like the very thing God had rejected.

The book of Judges is full of examples of Israel's desire to turn back to the ways of the nations (Judges 2:10-23, 4:1-4, 6:1-11, 8:33-35, 10:6-15, 13:1-5, 21:25). They would allow themselves to become corrupted and start becoming like what God had rejected, then God would bring discipline on them.

▶ Exercise:

Read 2 Kings 17:7-23.

List the ways that Israel turned away from the Lord: ____________________

____

____

List the ways that God brought discipline to Israel when the nation turned from Him: ____

____

____

Whenever Israel turned toward the nations,

- **Their hearts would shift from dependency and communion with God.**

  See to it, brothers, that none of you has a sinful, unbelieving heart that turns away from the living God. But encourage one another daily, as long as it is called Today, so that none of you may be hardened by sin's deceitfulness.

  Hebrews 3:12-14

- **They would become disobedient and begin to compromise the standards of God, and**

  The word of the Lord came to me: "Son of man, these men have set up idols in their hearts and put wicked stumbling blocks before their faces…tell them, 'This is what the

> Sovereign Lord says: ...Repent! Turn from your idols and renounce all your detestable practices!'"
>
> Ezekial 14:1-6

- **They would begin to live like the other nations and become idolatrous of heart.**

> If you ever forget the Lord your God and follow other gods and worship and bow down to them, I testify against you today that you will surely be destroyed. Like the nations the Lord destroyed before you, so you will be destroyed for not obeying the Lord your God.
>
> Deuteronomy 8:19-20

God would then begin to discipline them. He often gave Israel over in battle and allowed the nations to rule over, torment, and oppress them. He sent prophets crying out to the people to change. He would discipline Israel to get their attention, warn them that they were prostituting themselves, and send plagues and other things to draw them back to Himself (Judges 2:1-3,3:12-15, Amos 4:6-11,5:4-6).

> See, I set before you today life and prosperity, death and destruction. For I command you today to love the Lord your God, to walk in his ways, and to keep his commands, decrees and laws; then you will live and increase, and the Lord your God will bless you in the land you are entering to possess. But if your heart turns away and you are not obedient, and if you are drawn away to bow down to other gods and worship them, I declare to you this day that you will certainly be destroyed. You will not live long in the land you are crossing the Jordan to enter and possess.
>
> Deuteronomy 30:15-18

God's Purposes Burn in His Heart. Because of His great love and His covenant with Israel, God would warn them over and over of the consequences of their actions, and then He would say to them, "Return to me. I will heal you. I will cleanse you of your sins" (Isaiah 1). He would plead with them, "Walk in My ways and My purposes. Fulfill the mandate that I've given you. Follow my laws, commands, and decrees. Come back to me." He did all this in an attempt to draw Israel back to Himself and to the purposes for which the nation was created (Psalm 81, Jeremiah 3:12-19, Hosea 14:1-9).

Many times, Israel would repent and turn back to the Lord and His ways; they would have times of reviving and renewal (Hezekiah, for example; see 2 Chronicles 29-32). But it would not be long before they departed again; their hearts would turn away, they would begin to become disobedient and to serve other gods and become like the other nations (Deuteronomy 30:17-18, 2 Chronicles 24, Jeremiah 2:1-28).

Israel continued to reject God's purposes that they be set apart from the nations. They did not want to be set apart as His people; they wanted to be like the other nations—and God rejected them.

▶ **Exercise:**

How does this reality apply to the church today? ______________________

____

____

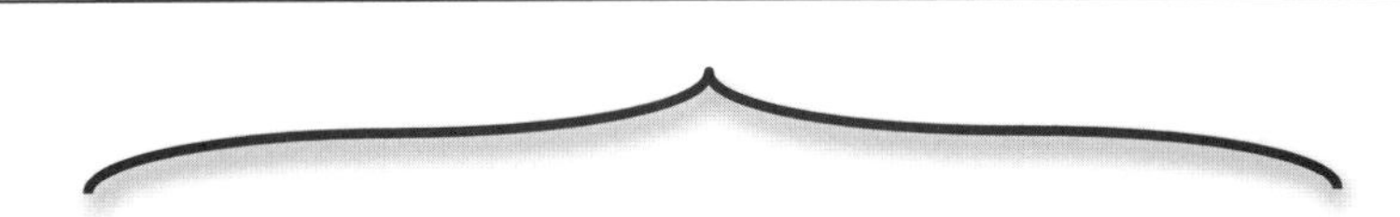

We grieve God the same way when we return to our own ways or the ways of the world. Many times we return to the very ways that He called us out of in the first place, just as Israel did.

The Redemption of Israel. Israel *was* like all the other nations. It didn't matter how much God blessed them, they didn't have it in them to do the work that He required of them; they couldn't fulfill the mission and purposes for which He had created them. So God had another aspect to His mission for Israel; through them He would send a Redeemer. He would come to His people Himself and work His plan of salvation (Isaiah 59). Out of Israel, all the nations of the world would be blessed. Out of Israel, He would say to the nations, "Come to me, all you who are weary and burdened, and I will give you rest" (Matthew 11:28).

Time for Reflection:

What do we learn from this era? What does God reject? What does He require? ______________________

What does God want you to do in response to this? ______________________

As you pray your prayer target for this day/week, what are you feeling the Holy Spirit is saying or calling you to and what is the warfare coming against you? ______________________

▸ Time for Prayer:

Can you say that you are seeking the Lord with all your heart? Spend time with the Lord, allowing Him to show you anything that is holding you back. Lay these things before Him and ask Him to set your life apart for His purposes, to bring you into a deeper level of surrender and trust. Abandon yourself to Him. Don't be tempted to stop praying too soon; keep praying until you have broken through and touched His heart.

Lesson 4.

God's Redemptive Plan: A Savior, the Church, and the Day of the Lord

Like Adam and the nations, Israel fell. The nation failed to fulfill the intentions for which God had created it. Israel became lost, and God allowed the people to be scattered and oppressed by the nations (2 Kings 17:1-23). Jerusalem was left in ruins and only a small remnant remained; the leaders of Babylon and surrounding nations desecrated the Temple, carried off all the treasures and wealth of Israel, and took the people captive back to their countries (2 Kings 25:1-21).

God looked at Israel and analyzed the situation. He could say to them, "This is not what I created you for. You are not set apart or different from the nations; you have become *like* the nations. You have veered off course; you have lost sight of my mission and what you were commissioned to do. You are not walking in your mandate." And then He moved into a new era and He sent Jesus, who came with a clear, undeniable mission: to redeem all mankind.

Era 4 — The Savior, Jesus Christ

Jesus came to call forth the church. The day He was born, the angels declared that He was the Savior of all people, not just Israel: "I bring you good news of great joy that will be for all people" (Luke 2:10). The angels brought good news to *all* men. Unlike Israel, Jesus submitted to every instruction from the Lord. For example, as He was getting baptized, John the Baptist asked Him, '"Why should we do this?" and Jesus said, "Because it is written." It was what the Father wanted, and Jesus did it so the scripture would be fulfilled.

Jesus' Complete Submission to the Mission of God. Jesus was totally dependent on the Father. He did everything the Father asked. He was completely focused on the Father's mission. He had a deep communion with God and was in total submission and dependency on Him. He was destroying the works of the devil. He was tempted and tested, but He continually chose the way of God. You can even see this submission and obedience in the ministry of Jesus.

▸ **Exercise:**

How do the following scriptures show that Jesus was committed to God's mission?

Luke 22:42: ______________________________

____

____

John 6:38: ______________________________

____

____

John 14:10,24: ______________________________

____

____

Luke 4:42-43: ______________________________

____

____

Jesus didn't veer from the mission at all. Everything God said, He did; He submitted to it. He gave Himself to it. He didn't treat it like it could be compromised. He did exactly what God said.

And because of His surrender, complete obedience, and total trust in the Father, His mission was successful, and through Him, all the nations have the opportunity to be redeemed.

God's Redemptive Purposes in the Nations. Near the end of His life, one of the final acts Jesus did to complete His mission was to call forth the church, which would include both Israelites and Gentiles. God's eternal purpose is to redeem and restore all men, not just the one nation. In Romans, Paul tells us that God grafted in the Gentiles. He wants us to rise up in such a way that it provokes envy in Israel; where Israel is jealous for what God is doing among the church (Romans 11:11).

During His years of ministry, Jesus had raised a band of men, a few disciples, who He could train, send, and commission. He could ask this small group to take on the mission of God, to fulfill God's heart desires. Jesus initially sent them to the lost sheep of Israel, but then He sent them to the whole world, to teach the nations everything He had commanded. He promised the disciples that they would receive power from on high to do the work they were being called to do, then He sent them out to disciple the nations and draw people back to communion with God.

Jesus came to earth on a mission that He never strayed from, and near the end, He looked at Israel and wept, saying, "I wanted to draw you in like a mother hen does her chicks, but you missed your time of visitation" (Matthew 23:37, Luke 13:34). Israel had again turned from God, so through Jesus, God's mandate was to raise up the church that would fulfill His purposes.

Era 5 – The Church

God is still on a mission to draw the nations back to Himself. With the coming of the Messiah was the birth of a new people: the church. Every element of society in the nations and Israel had become corrupted and defiled, and God – who had rejected their way of life – was now turning to the church to redeem them.

The church has a great task: we are sent to "Go into the world and preach the gospel to all nations" (Matthew 28:19-20). God has given us directions and instructions. He taught us how to pray and how to walk in dependency and communion with Him. He has revealed His heart's desires to us, and given us all power and authority to fulfill His mission (Matthew 28:17-19).

> Therefore go and make disciples of all nations, baptizing them in the name of the Father and of the Son and of the Holy Spirit, and teaching them to obey everything I have commanded you.
> Matthew 28:19-20

What is the Church's Mission? Below are just a few scriptures that describe the Father's intent, objectives, and mission for the church.

▸ Exercise:

Read the text on the following three pages two times out loud. Prayerfully allow the Holy Spirit to write these truths on your heart.

THE CHURCH IS TO BE THE GLOBAL, REDEEMED PEOPLE OF GOD

We are set apart and do not live under the power of sin, the old nature, or Satan:

- **Romans 6:6-7:**
  - My old self was crucified so that the body of sin might be done away, that I should no longer be a slave to sin
  - I died with Christ and to the power of sin's rule over my life
- **Romans 6:10-11:**
  - I count myself dead to sin but alive to God in Christ Jesus
- **Romans 6:22:**
  - I have been set free from sin and have become a slave to God
- **Romans 8:2-4:**
  - Through Christ Jesus the law of the Spirit of life set me free from the law of sin and death
  - I do not live according to the sinful nature but according to the Spirit
- **Romans 8:13:**
  - If by the Spirit I put to death the misdeeds of the body, I will live
- **2 Corinthians 5:**
  - Since I have died, I no longer live for myself but for Christ
  - I am a new creation and have a divine nature
- **1 John 5:18:**
  - I have been born of God and therefore do not continue to sin
  - Jesus keeps me safe; the evil one cannot harm me

We are covenanted to God as His children and called by His name

- **John 1:12-13:**
  - Because I have received him, because I have believed in His name, He has given me the right to become a child of God—a child born not of natural descent, but born of God
- **Romans 8:14-17:**
  - I am led by the Spirit of God and am therefore a child of God
  - I did not receive a spirit that makes me a slave again to fear; I have received the Spirit of sonship
  - By Him I cry, "Abba, Father"
  - The Spirit himself testifies with my spirit that I am God's child
  - If I am a child, then I am an heir—an heir of God and a co-heir with Christ
  - Everything that belongs to Jesus Christ belongs to me
  - I share in His sufferings in order that I may also share in His glory

- **Galatians 3:29:**
  - If I belong to Christ, then I am an heir according to the promise
- **Galatians 4:5-6:**
  - I will receive the full rights of a child
  - Because I am His child, God sent the Spirit of His Son into my heart, the Spirit who calls out, "Abba, Father"
- **1 John 3:1-2:**
  - How great is the love the Father has lavished on me, that I should be called a child of God! And that is what I am!
  - I am a child of God
  - What I will be has not yet been made known, but I know that when He appears, I shall be like Him

God has called us out of the system and patterns of this world

- **Matthew 5:14 & Philippians 2:20:**
  - I am the light of the world that shines forth His glory in this dark world
- **John 15:19:**
  - I do not belong to the world, but God has chosen me out of the world
- **John 17:16:**
  - I am not of the world
- **Romans 12:2:**
  - I will not conformed any longer to the pattern of this world, but will be transformed by the renewing of my mind
- **Ephesians 2:2:**
  - I no longer follow the ways of the world
- **1 John 2:15:**
  - I do not love the world

We are called to reveal His glory, His love, His righteousness, and His Kingdom authority on earth

- **John 13:35:**
  - If I love others, all men will know that I am His disciple
- **John 15:1-8:**
  - I am to remain in Christ and be a channel of Christ's life, bearing forth much fruit
- **2 Corinthians 8:24:**
  - I will love people so that the others can see it
- **1 John 3:16:**
  - This is how I know what love is: Jesus Christ laid down his life for me
  - I will lay down my life for my brothers
- **1 Peter 4:13:**
  - I rejoice that I participate in the sufferings of Christ
  - I will be overjoyed when His glory is revealed

We are called to fulfill His purposes among men

- **John 15:8,16:**
  - I did not choose Him; He chose me
  - He appointed me to bear much fruit, showing myself to be His disciple
- **Acts 26:16:**

    - God has appointed me as a servant and a witness of what I have seen of Him and what He will show me
- **Ephesians 1:11:**
    - In Him I was also chosen, having been predestined according to the plan of Him who works out everything in conformity with the purpose of His will
- **Ephesians 3:10-11:**
    - His intent was that the manifold wisdom of God should be made known to the rulers and authorities in the heavenly realms, according to His eternal purpose

We are Christ's ambassadors, sent forth to reconcile the lost world to its Creator

- **John 15:16:**
    - God chose me and appointed me to go and bear fruit
- **Acts 1:8:**
    - I will be God's witness in Jerusalem, and in all Judea and Samaria, and to the ends of the earth
- **2 Corinthians 5:18-20:**
    - God, who reconciled me to Himself through Christ, gave me the ministry of reconciliation: that God was reconciling the world to Himself in Christ
    - I am therefore Christ's ambassador, as though God were making His appeal through me

We are the army of God, sent into the earth to destroy the works of the devil and lead people out of the darkness and into the light

- **Mark 16:17:**
    - I have authority over all dark forces
- **John 14:12:**
    - I am called to do the works Jesus did, and even greater
- **Acts 26:17-18:**
    - God is sending me out to open blind eyes and turn people from darkness to light and from the power of Satan to God, so that they may receive forgiveness of sins and a place among those who are sanctified by faith in Christ
- **Hebrews 2:14-15:**
    - Since God's children are flesh and blood, Christ shared in their humanity so that by His death he might destroy the devil, who holds the power of death, and free us, who have been held in slavery by our fear of death

Corporately, we are the Bride of Christ—called to be pure, spotless, and blameless—preparing Creation for the coming of the Day of the Lord

- 2 Corinthians 11:2:
    - God has promised me to one husband, to Christ, so that He might present me as a pure virgin to Him
- **Philippians 1:9-11:**
    - I am to be pure and blameless until the day of Christ
- **Revelation 19:7:**
    - The wedding of the Lamb has come and as His bride, I have made myself ready

What is the covenantal position of the church? ____________________

____

____

We have been given all authority in heaven and earth, and been made joint heirs with Jesus Christ. We are to see the kingdom and will of God established on all the earth. We are to be the redeemed people of God who do not live under the power of sin, the flesh, or Satan, but under the power of the Holy Spirit. We are covenanted to God to be His children, to walk in His authority, to have direct access to Him. We have been given access to the very throne of God and are assured of His welcome. We have been given a mantle of authority and are to live in such a way as to reveal God's glory, love, and character to the whole earth.

What has the church been commissioned to do? ____________________

____

____

The church does not exist just to do good deeds; it has been given a clear mission from God. We are His ambassadors, sent forth to reconcile the world unto Him. We are to destroy the works of the enemy, and draw people out of the darkness and into the light. We are called to prepare the world for the day of His coming, and to be a pure, spotless bride that knows this world is fading away, and therefore are to live ready, waiting, and speeding His coming. This is the purpose for which we live.

What gifts and promises has the church been given? ____________________

____

____

We have been given the indwelling presence of the Holy Spirit and been made joint heirs with Jesus Christ. Everything that belongs to Him belongs to the church. God has promised that we are more than conquerors through Christ Jesus, that there is no weapon formed against us that would prosper, that the One who is in us is greater than the one who is in the world, that He would never leave us or forsake us, that His grace is sufficient to meet all of our needs, that we would destroy the works of the devil, that we will do even greater things than

He has done, and that as He builds the church, the gates of Hell cannot prosper against it. These are just a few of the promises that God has given to the church.

What are the instructions and commands God gave the church? ________

____

____

We are to love God with all our hearts and to love others as Christ has loved us. We are not to love the world and chase after things of the world. The church is to be known for its radical love for others; it is to be our distinctive—what makes us unique and how the world will know that we are His disciples. Everything hangs on these two: our love for God and our love for one another. People will see the way that the church loves—that we are sacrificial, generous, compassionate, merciful, devoted, abandoned, completely given over to God and captivated by His love—and they will be drawn to the church because of its radical love for God and for people.

What Are We to Do? The church is to be the hope of the nations. We are to be the ones who are pushing back the darkness and making a way for the light to shine out. The church is to be carrying a love that is so radical and sacrificial that men know that we are God's disciples. We are to carry an authority that is greater than the darkness and that can break the bondages and captivities that are imprisoning nations in this day and time. We are to be walking in the wisdom, power, and authority of Jesus Christ that is beginning to confound even the dark forces that seek to undermine the purposes and will of God on the earth. We are to be seeing His kingdom be established and the power of darkness beginning to be broken. The church is to be the light that dispels the darkness, the salt that preserves the culture, and the hope that radiates forth into the nations. That is what Jesus died to give the church.

▸ Exercise:

As you read about what Christ purchased for the church and what He made available for us to be, then you see the condition of the church and the nations, what kind of reaction does that cause in your heart? ___

____

____

When you look at the other eras, seeing how the people began to drift further and further away from their mission, and you realize that God created the church because Israel was not fulfilling its mission, what kind of reaction does that cause in your heart? ____________________

____

____

Situation Analysis

If God took a situation analysis of today's church, what would He say? We took a poll of about 200 people from 10 different nations; below are some of their responses:

- We are in a state of slumber
- We have compromised God's standards
- We have relied on human wisdom instead of God's wisdom
- We are failing as ambassadors of Christ to redeem the nations to Christ
- We are not walking in the power, authority, and understanding that Christ died to give us
- We are not opening the eyes of the blind, setting the captives free, or healing the broken-hearted
- We have lost the focus and main purpose of why Christ laid His life down: to disciple the nations
- We have failed to teach and disciple the nations
- We have taken ministry as doing good activities and failed to work to fulfill God's heart desire
- We spend very little time in the Word of God and therefore have very little understanding of what it says, the instructions it gives, etc
- We have failed to follow the instructions God gave us, and are therefore not standing in our covenant position with Him
- We have strayed far away from the church revealed in Acts, in which everyone shared what they had and no one was in need
- We have failed to seek God's will and have therefore become irrelevant in the nations
- We can no longer affect Creation; therefore, the Creation is in agony and bondage
- We have not kept our purity as a Bride of Christ
- We are failing to blow the trumpet and warn the people of the coming of the day of the Lord
- We have lost our first love

Is the Church Fulfilling Its Mission? When we see what Christ envisioned and provided for the church and the church becoming more and more worldly, diminished, rejected, and alienated, it should break our hearts. In many nations, the church is having minimal impact. The nations are being shaken, darkness is coming in like a flood, sin is eating away at our societies like a plague, and the spirit of slumber is blinding and incapacitating the church, keeping it from standing and fighting the darkness effectively.

The church has lost sight of its mission. We have gotten busy running programs and showing up for services. The majority have become spectators and consumers of Christianity instead of missionaries and ambassadors of Jesus Christ. We have begun to settle for the rhetoric of victory and power, but not the reality of real victory. The hour is growing late, the darkness is increasing, and yet the church is in a state of lethargy. This is not the position Jesus died to give the church. There must be an urgency growing in our hearts.

Sometimes, when we face such disparagement between what we are called to be and what we actually are, we can feel like it is too much to deal with; we almost become paralyzed and give up. We don't even rise up to fight; we feel hopeless and see reason to react because we are so far away from what was intended. It just feels too big to do anything about. We must fight this tendency.

An example in the Bible of someone who saw similar disparagement between God's ways and the way that the people were living was King Josiah.

▶ **Exercise:**

Read 2 Kings 22-23. What was King Josiah's reaction when he realized what God had called Israel to be and where they actually were? ________

____

____

When the book of the law was found and read to the king, he tore his garments and cried out to God. When he saw the spiritual state of the nation, and the state of the temple and the people—how far Israel had strayed from what God had called them to be—something began to seize his heart. He could no longer accept or tolerate the status quo. He began to cry out and do whatever he could to see things be brought back to what God had intended.

▶ Our Heart's Response:

Pause a few moments for prayer. Cry out for God's mercy. Ask God to give us a heart that is not just stirred in this moment, to not allow us to fall back into apathy, and to help us be willing to do whatever it takes for Him to turn this tide and begin to change this course. Journal anything that the Holy Spirit shows you: ______________________

____

____

Era 6 — The Day of the Lord

When you read the scriptures, you can clearly see the sequence of the eras. You can also see that as the church era comes to an end, there is only one era left: the Day of the Lord.

Through our studies, we have come to see that although it has had 2,000 years, the church is not fulfilling the mission that God created it for; we have also seen how God has dealt with that through the ages. When we have a true understanding of what the next era is and believe with certainty that it is truly almost upon us, our hearts should tremble.

When we recognize what the scriptures say about the Day of the Lord and all that it entails, we know that we cannot afford to miss this wake-up call. The church must arise; we must not miss our time, as Israel missed its time of visitation with the Messiah.

It has been thousands of years since God called Abram out to be the father of a nation. Less than a few thousand years ago, Jesus came, the Holy Spirit was given, and the church was commissioned. God has given us time to go to the nations. But now the Day is near and the judgments are beginning to come upon the earth. Wickedness is suffocating the nations. People no longer know the difference between right and wrong, holy and unholy, because the line has become so blurred. There is a rise of deception. The time is growing late.

All throughout scripture, in the Old Testament as well as the New Testament, the last era is what scripture refers to as "the last days," "the Day," "the Day of the Lord," and sometimes "the Day of wrath" or "the Day of the Lord's anger." What does scripture mean by this? It is referred to as three different things:

1. The era of time referred to in scripture when there is a building toward the battle between the powers of darkness and the powers of light,
2. A day of wrath or judgment, and
3. The last day; the day the Lord will appear.

We are drawing near the era of time called the last days. Scriptures say that as the final era draws near, many things will begin to take place (2 Timothy 3:1-5): deception and wickedness will increase, people will be more and more easily wounded and offended, and the love of many will grow cold. People will become more unforgiving and lack self-control; there will be more addictions, more complaining; negativity will increase; people will grow more greedy, selfish, arrogant, and self-serving. They will begin to develop theologies that make them comfortable in their compromise, and they will have a form of religion, but it will be devoid of power to break the forces of darkness and set people free.

▶ Exercise

Do you see these things increasing in our day and time? If so, explain. __

____

____

____

As time grows late, people are becoming more demanding of their rights; we are lowering the standards of God, even in the church; people are becoming boastful and proud, even making statements that we don't need God anymore; people have become self-absorbed and have little time or energy to really pursue God with all their heart. These things are increasing in our day. Like a plague of locusts, they come in and devour our lands.

God even tells us that what happened to Israel is a warning to us; they are "examples to keep us from setting our hearts on evil things as they did" (1 Corinthians 10:1-11). He warns us not to be idolaters or indulge in pagan celebrations, to be sexually pure, and to avoid grumbling. Israel did all these things and many died. The Bible says "their bodies were scattered over the desert." "These things happened to them as examples" and warnings; they are to keep us from turning away from God as the Israelites did. They are to keep us from falling into darkness and losing our ability to fulfill the purposes of God.

> Nevertheless, God was not pleased with most of them; their bodies were scattered over the desert. Now these things occurred as examples to keep us from setting our hearts on evil things as they did. Do not be idolaters, as some of them were; as it is written: "The people sat down to eat and drink and got up to indulge in pagan revelry." We should not commit sexual immorality, as some of them did—and in one day twenty-three thousand of them died. We should not test the Lord, as some of them did—and were killed by snakes. And do not grumble, as some of them did—and were killed by the destroying angel. These things happened to them as examples and were written down as warnings for us, on whom the fulfillment of the ages has come.
>
> 1 Corinthians 10:1-11

Beloved, we need to respond now. We need to join with others so we can begin to see a fire building that will help bring awakening, because the forces of darkness that we have just described are only going to increase as the time grows late. There is no return after the final era, the Day of the Lord. This is the reason for the urgency of the hour.

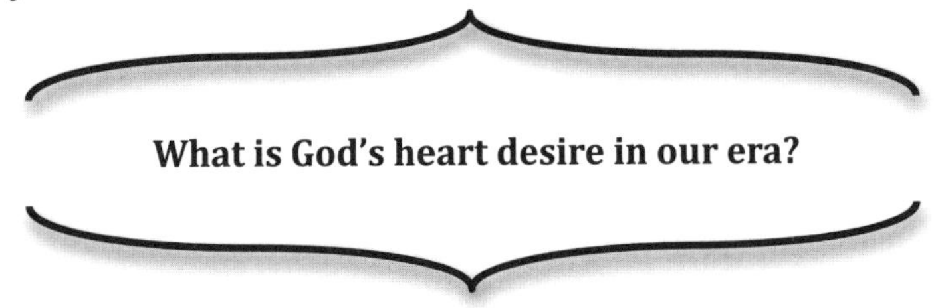

This is the key question. We have been learning over the past 2 weeks that we must capture God's heart if we are going to be able to do the work that He is requiring of us. When you look at the eras of time and what God has been seeking to do, and you see the impending Day of the Lord,

What is burning in God's heart?______________________________

____

____

What does the church need to be doing and being about? ___________

God is raising a remnant, an army (Joel 2:1-11). This is a new army that has never existed and will never exist again; an army that is sold out to the Lord, willing to not only live for Him but also to die for Him. The people in this army understand the odds, what is at stake, the heart of God. He will hand-pick each one of them and draw their hearts to Himself. This army is becoming dissatisfied with the status quo and something deep inside of them is beginning to groan for the Lord. Some are children, some adults; some are rich, some poor; some are educated, some illiterate – but God is bringing their hearts to be one.

As God calls out this army, He is going to set it on fire and send it out to the nations. The church is going to be revived and changed; it will throw off the things of the world. The church will begin to rise up in what it was commissioned to be—what Christ died for it to be—in greater fullness of its power and authority.

The Day of the Lord is coming. The Lord is working to prepare His own. We can see the mission of the Father. We can see the intentions of His heart. His goals and purposes are clear.

You are not here by accident. God is calling us to this army. Let us understand the standards of the Lord. Let us see the ways of life that God has rejected. Let us not be deceived by the allures of the world. God is calling us for "such a time as this."

▶ **Exercise:**

Will we go with Him? ___________

What will be the cost if we don't? ___________

What Must We Do to Work the Works That God Requires?

We must begin to abandon ourselves and allow God to raise us up as His army. We need to give ourselves in surrender to Him, knowing that only He can make us ready, to strengthen us so we can stand against the forces and the battles that will come, to give us the wisdom we need to go forward. We have to turn our backs on the world and give ourselves to seeking the Lord with all our hearts, rejecting the compromises and apostasy being taught today and seeking the age-old truth of the Bible. We must choose to give ourselves fully to the Lord and His ways so His purposes can be fulfilled through our lives.

This is the call of the hour. Let us set ourselves apart for the Lord and allow Him to work deeply in our lives to prepare us for the times ahead. He will do in us what we cannot do for ourselves and will bring us to the fulfillment of our calling and destiny in the world.

Time for Reflection:

What do we learn from this era? What does God reject? What does He require? ____________________

What does God want you to do in response to this? ____________________

As you pray your prayer target for this day/week, what are you feeling the Holy Spirit is saying or calling you to and what is the warfare coming against you? ____________________

Prayer Targets

Remember that each day's prayer targets should give you things to "walk out." We are fighting for a spiritual position, a spiritual reality we're seeking to come into, and as we begin to gain the ground in the spiritual realm we will begin to impact the physical realm. The prayer targets are therefore an essential part of the study because you will be seeking to gain ground in the spiritual realm, which will begin to give you authority, insight, and understanding to be able to impact the physical realm.

What Does It Mean to "Pray Into" a Position?

When God has revealed that there is something more He wants to lead us into, we must give ourselves to "praying (ourselves) into" that position. We know that God is calling us to a deeper place and that we are not yet "there." As we are seeking to gain this new ground, we must hold up the things that God has said, who He is, and what He has done. We proclaim His faithfulness for all that He *has* done—and we pray into believing that He *will do* what we know He is saying that He will do.

We will be speaking a lot in the next few weeks about "praying into" position. It is important that we apply this concept to our daily prayer life; otherwise, we won't be fighting to gain the ground the Lord is giving us, we will not have the insight we need, and we will therefore be unprepared and ill-equipped for the work that He is calling us to do.

▸ Time for Prayer:

Ask the Lord to impress upon your heart the urgency of the hour. Ask Him to give you insight and understanding into His hearts' desires for this era of time. What is He calling you to do? How is He calling you to join Him in His work? Are you willing to be part of the army that He is rising up? What within you resists giving yourself fully to God and His work? Do business with the Father today. Spend as much time as needed to come to the place where you can surrender yourself fully to being a vessel that He can use to fulfill His purposes in our day. Begin to "pray into" a place of abandonment and trust before the Lord, yielded and willing to give your life to fulfill His heart's desires.

Week 4.

The Process by Which God Works

GOAL OF THE WEEK:

This week we want to
1. Understand the process by which God determines the work that He is going to do

2. Yield ourselves to God in order to be a vessel through which He can do His work

As we look at the eras we discussed last week, you can clearly see where God was working. You can see that He has an overall mission, and that it does not change from era to era. In addition, as you study these eras more closely, you begin to notice that there is a pattern to the way that God works. We want to understand that pattern so that we can cooperate with God and begin to allow Him to use us to accomplish His purposes.

We've asked several questions over and over again each and every week:
- How do we join God in His work?
- How do we begin to recognize and fulfill His heart desires?
- How do we begin to allow Him to do His work through us?
- *What shall we do, that we may work the works of God?*

This week, we're going to begin to look closely at the pattern by which God works through individuals and groups of people so that we can begin to come into His purposes.

Prayer targets for week 4:

1. Help me understand and abandon myself to Your ways.

2. Give me eyes to see what You are showing me so that I can be the vessel You need me to be to do Your work.

Audio/video link for week 4:

http://worldtrumpet.org/awakening-the-church
(week 4)

Lesson 1.
The Process God Follows

When reading through the Bible, you begin to identify five key elements in the process of the way that God works:

1. **Situation analysis:** God looks over a situation and contrasts it to His heart desires. He does not judge situations on how good they look or feel, but He looks at the situation in contrast with His heart plan to see if it is aligned with what He had intended.
2. **God's mission:** Once He sees the situation and how it is related to His heart desire, He makes a plan to intervene and lays out a mission to bring the situation back into line with His heart purposes.
3. **God's intended goals and objectives:** Once He has made a situation analysis and determined His mission, God then sets clear goals that will result in the fulfillment of that mission.
4. **God's chosen vessel:** Once the Lord has set goals for Himself, He chooses a vessel through which He will work to accomplish His mission. This releases the destiny of that vessel.
5. **God's mandate:** God bestows His power and authority on the vessel He has chosen to go and pursue the work. There are six things that are part of the mandate, which we will discuss next week:
6. **God's commissioning:** God sends someone out and directs them to do a certain task. In short, commissioning is being told, "Go and do."
    a. **Catching the vision of God's heart:** Being able to see into God's heart. Knowing His heart desires and understanding how to fulfill them.
    b. **Covenantal position:** The covenantal position is a tangible place where your heart is surrendered and completely trusting in Him.
    c. **God's commandments and instructions:** These are instructions the Lord gives, which, when followed, protect us, keep us going in the right direction, make us fruitful, etc.
    d. **God's gifts and promises**
    e. **God's grace and anointing to do the work**

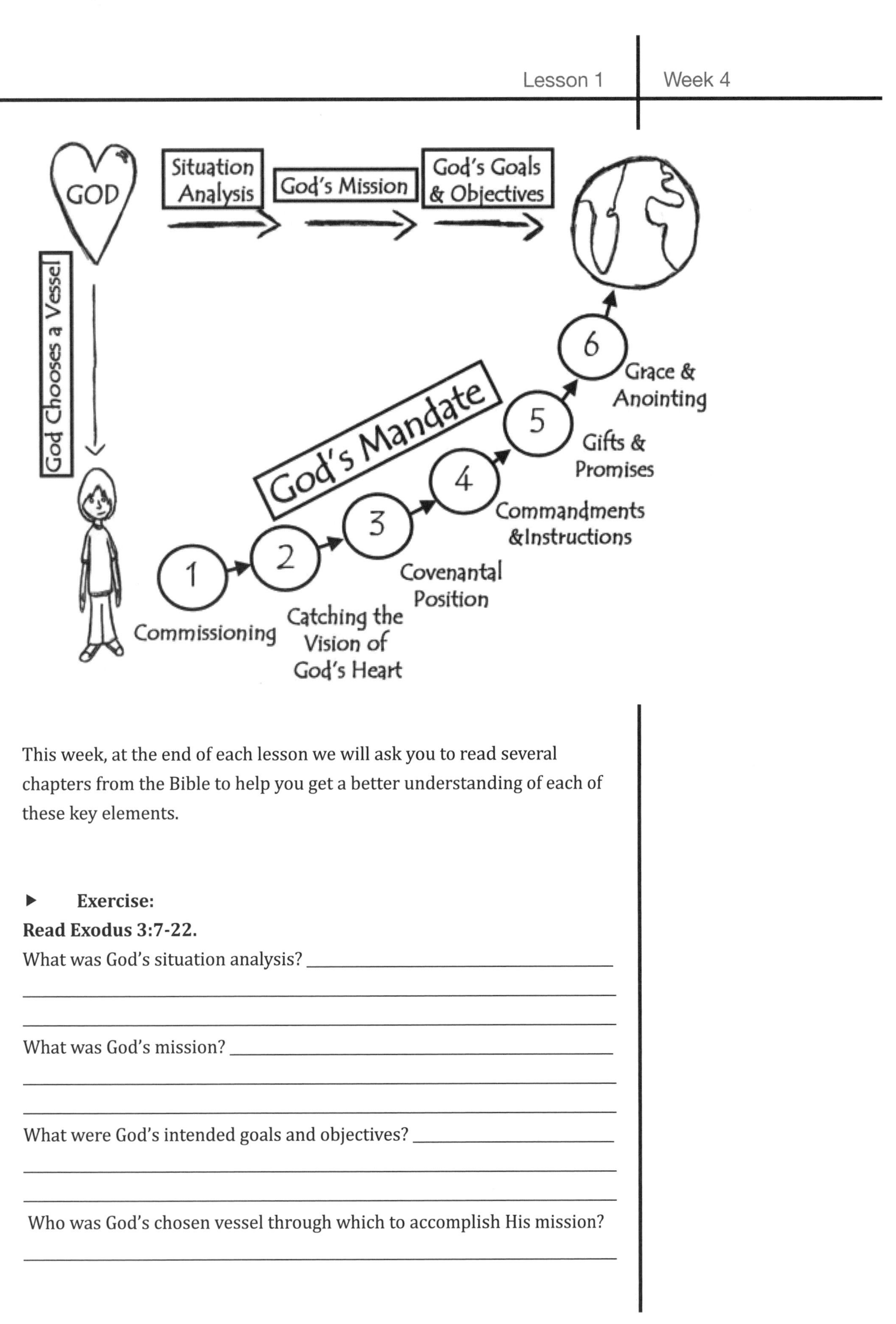

This week, at the end of each lesson we will ask you to read several chapters from the Bible to help you get a better understanding of each of these key elements.

▶ **Exercise:**

Read Exodus 3:7-22.

What was God's situation analysis? ______________________________

____

____

What was God's mission? ______________________________

____

____

What were God's intended goals and objectives? ______________________________

____

____

Who was God's chosen vessel through which to accomplish His mission?

____

The first thing God does is analyze a situation and pass verdict over it. He had seen the misery of His people and was concerned about their suffering. He set a mission to rescue them and bring them into the Promised Land. He set goals of bringing the people out of Egypt, striking the Egyptians with His might until Pharaoh let them go, and plundering the Egyptians of their wealth. Finally, God involved Moses to join Him in this work. This was the destiny for which Moses had been created.

Many times when the Lord desires to correct a particular problem or fulfill part of His overall purposes, He works through the discernable process outlined and discussed above. If God sees a situation and because of that situation He sets out to do something about it, He sets a mission for Himself. That means He must have certain goals He wants to see at the end of that mission. It's very important to capture God's vision—His mission and heart as well as the goals that He has set. Why? Because if we are doing what we know God has called us to do, but what we are doing is not changing the situation that He analyzed in the beginning—it is not bringing about God's vision—it means our ministry is not having impact. Understanding this process will help us understand how we can join God is His work. Some examples of this process are discussed below.

if we are doing what we know God has called us to do, but what we are doing is not changing the situation that He analyzed in the beginning—it is not bringing about God's vision—it means our ministry is not having impact.

The Five Elements of the Process That God Follows

Situation Analysis. God looks at a situation and determines if it is meeting the desires of His heart. If the situation is not in line with what He had intended, He will first make a verdict of the situation, and then will proceed to formulate a mission, set goals and objectives, and choose a vessel through which He can bring the situation back in line with what He had intended.

- **Establishing Israel:** One example of this is God's mission to raise up the nation of Israel. After the flood, the Lord had again given man the commandment to "be fruitful and multiply" (Genesis 9:7). He wanted man to increase in number and cover the whole earth. This was the same command given to Adam in Genesis 1:28. God wanted man to spread out and fill the earth, which would result in people groups in all parts of the globe. The story of the tower of Babel shows us that the people resisted this command (Genesis 11:4); Instead, they decided to build a city with a tower so they would not be scattered over the face of the earth. So God confused their language and forced them to scatter. At the same time, He recognized that man's heart was inclined to evil (Genesis 8:21); any nations formed by man would be corrupt because they were corrupt.

- **Moses Delivers Israel From Egypt:** Another example of God making a situation analysis is when He heard the cries of the Hebrews, who had been enslaved in Egypt for over 400 years. God remembered the covenant He had made with Abraham more than 400 years earlier, and knew that the time had come for Israel to be set free from slavery and brought into the land He had promised them (Genesis 15:5-21).

God's Mission. God's mission is what He is going to do to bring things back to His original plan. God begins to move into the situation, breaks whatever has been maintaining it, changes and converts whatever has been distorted or corrupted, and then brings it back in line with what He had intended. This is His mission and work. If God is going to involve us in His work, it will be within this process.

- **Establishing Israel:** After analyzing the condition of man's heart and the nations of the earth, God set a mission to establish a nation of people that would be His. Through this nation God would demonstrate His character and righteousness to the other nations. It would be a nation that He could lead, that would obey and follow His commandments and instructions; this nation would be set apart and holy, like no other nation on the earth. By following Him and His ways, this nation would not be corrupted as the other nations were. God would bring redemption to the nations of the earth through this one nation, so He set a mission for Himself to create Israel, a nation of people that would be His.

- **Moses Delivers Israel From Egypt:** When the Lord heard the cries of His people, who were in slavery in Egypt, he analyzed the situation. Remembering that He had promised the land of Canaan to Abraham, and knowing that the wickedness of the Amorites had reached its full measure (Genesis 15:16), He set a mission for Himself to set the people free, to bring Israel out of slavery and into the land He had promised them (Exodus 3:7-8).

God's Intended Goals and Objectives: God has goals and objectives that He desires to accomplish in His mission. These are landmarks in what God is going to be doing. He begins with one goal, which will lead to another, and then another until it comes to the end and His mission has been fulfilled. Identifying these things will show us the targets of God. When we are called to be a part of God's work, we need to see where we are standing in the process and determine what God's targets are in that place, then we can measure our achievement in line with God's targets; otherwise, we can be busy doing things, but not be bearing any fruit.

- **Establishing Israel:** After God set a mission to create the nation of Israel, He also set clear goals and objectives. God wanted Israel to have a deep communion and dependency on Him, to fully know Him as their God. He wanted them to be a strong nation that would obey His commands and follow Him in battle. He would reveal Himself to them and teach them His ways. As they followed and obeyed, He would also show Himself to all the nations of the earth through them.

- **Moses Delivers Israel From Egypt:** The Lord's mission was to deliver Israel from bondage and take them into the Promised Land. While doing this, God would reveal to Israel and all the nations of the earth who He was; they would see His power, His provision, His security. They would see that He brought the victory; that His hand was on Israel. That the God of Israel was powerful, not to be trifled with. God would glorify Himself through Israel and reveal His power to the whole earth, then all the world would see and understand that when the Lord leads a people, He provides for them and is able to bring them into His purposes.

Once God has set His mission and goals, He chooses a vessel through which He can do His work.

God's Chosen Vessel: Once God has set His mission and goals, He chooses a vessel through which He can do His work. The vessel may be a man or a woman, a team or a church, a prophet or an intercessor. This is their destiny, their divine identity. It is what is written about them in the scroll. Destiny includes (1) calling, which is the purpose for which a person is created, and (2) the giftings, abilities, talents, and molding that God put inside that person which enables them to fulfill that calling.

- **Establishing Israel:** The Lord chose Abraham and commanded him to come away from the other people so He could make him into a nation for Himself. Abraham trusted God and so became the Father of the nation of Israel, helping to accomplish the mission that God had set for Himself.

- **Moses Delivers Israel From Egypt:** God chose Moses to be the vessel through which He would fulfill His mission of bringing the children of Israel out of Egypt, out of the slavery they had been in for over 400 years.

Yielding to God's Process

Because Abraham and Moses yielded themselves to God's purposes, because they desired to follow and obey His commands, God was able to fulfill His intended mission in both circumstances. He was also able to fill the goals and objectives that He had set. These landmarks reveal God's character to Israel and to the nations of the earth: His power, faithfulness, goodness, wrath, provision, security, etc. They also reveal that our God is timeless; that His mission is for all time and not for the moment. For example, through establishing a nation for Himself through Abraham, and then by saving that nation and bringing it into its destiny through Moses, God fulfilled the following desires of His heart:

- God chose for Himself a people out of the corrupt nations, a treasured possession (Deuteronomy 7:6)
- God showed Himself to Israel and the nations of the earth as mighty and as faithful (Deuteronomy 7:7-9)
- God blessed all the nations of the earth through Israel (Genesis 18:18; Galatians 3:8)
- God gave Israel His law and revealed His righteousness so all men would know they cannot meet His standards and realize they need a Savior (Exodus 20; Galatians 3:21-24)
- God brought a Savior and salvation to all nations through Israel (Genesis 18:18; Isaiah 59:20)
- God called a people to Himself through this Savior from all nations and established a new covenant with them; this is the birth of the church (Isaiah 49:6; Titus 2:14; 1 Peter 2:9)
- God will use the church to fulfill His overall mission of discipling the nations (Matthew 28:19)

Testimony: George Mueller

In the early 1800's, the faith in the people in Europe had fallen to incredibly low levels; they didn't believe God for anything. God looked at the situation and began to stir in George Mueller a desire to raise the level of faith in the people of England and cause them to want to know God. God continued to deepen this desire, this burden, within Mueller until he began to want to radically trust God to fill above and beyond his every need and for God to give him a means for people to see how real God is.

God gave George Mueller a mission: to begin to start orphanages and care for children in Bristol, England. God instructed Mueller to never ask anyone for contributions toward the care of these orphans or the schools that he had opened. He was to just pray and depend on God to provide.

George Mueller began to trust God in such tangible ways that nobody could deny that God was real and that He was at work. He housed, fed, clothed, and educated over 2,000 orphans annually, as well as supported the teachers and maintenance of the buildings. Mueller also supported more than 180 missionaries and distributed vast quantities of Bibles and tracts. He was able to do all these things through the support of others, but Mueller never asked anyone for a penny.

God wasn't seeking to just care for orphans; He had analyzed the situation in Europe at the time and saw that the faith of the people and the church had fallen away. He then commissioned a man named George Mueller who would radically trust Him and give himself to God, and watched as George Mueller showed the world that God was real and that He answered prayer.

During the more than 60 years that George Mueller trusted the Lord to provide for all his needs, he had received over $7.5 million dollars in answer to prayer and cared for thousands and thousands of orphans. In addition, Mueller's obedience opened the door for multitudes of others, such as Hudson Taylor, Charles Studd, DL Moody, and Charles Spurgeon, to go out on mission for God.

The fruit that can be born through a vessel humble and yielded to the Lord is beyond our comprehension. But let us be ready to be that vessel; let us be abandoned and prepared to be a vessel God would choose to accomplish His purposes in our day.

▶ **Exercise:**

Read the story of George Mueller above.

What was the mission God gave to George Mueller? ____________________

____

____

What goals and objectives did God fulfill through George Mueller? ________

____

____

Did George Mueller accomplish the mission God had set before him?______
Describe the fruit of George Mueller's ministry: ____________________

____

____

God commissioned George Mueller to "Go and cause the people around you to see that I am real, to trust me, and to believe that I am a prayer-answering God." George Mueller's destiny and calling—the purpose for which He was created—was to radically trust the Lord to provide not only for his personal needs, but also for the needs of the work God gave him to do, such as open orphanages and schools. Through answered prayer, God provided millions of dollars to George Mueller, revealing how real He is to the nations, that He could be trusted in every way, and that He answers prayer. This revived the faith of people throughout nations in his and future generations.

George Mueller gave himself fully to God and God was able to do something through him that could never be done through human means.

God analyzed the situation. George Mueller gave himself to God in the way that God wanted, and God was able to do something through him that could never be done through human means. And out of that, the objectives that God had set began to be fulfilled.

During the time of George Mueller, as people began to be stirred spiritually, many people rose up who affected the times, who brought awakening and revival to the territory God gave them. Out of that era whole missionary movements began, and faith began to come alive again. Hudson Taylor founded the China Inland Mission, which sent 800 missionaries to China, began over 100 schools, and witnessed almost 20,000 conversions. His contemporaries, Charles Spurgeon and D.L. Moody, supported the China Inland Mission and encouraged their congregations to volunteer for overseas mission work. William Booth founded the Salvation Army, which today has a presence in over 120 nations around the world.

If the work you are doing for God is not bringing about change, if it is not meeting the goals and objectives that God set—if it is not fulfilling God's heart desires—you must go back and cry out for the Lord to reveal where you have strayed and to lead you back to the place where He can work through you.

Measuring Our Fruitfulness

As we serve God, we need to assess whether we are being fruitful. Paul said to the Corinthians, "But if we judged ourselves, we would not come under judgment" (1 Corinthians 11:31). We need to periodically examine what we're doing and whether it's consistent with God's mission. We also need to periodically examine whether we're accomplishing the results He intended when He chose us to join Him in His work.

If the work you are doing for God is not bringing about change, if it is not meeting the goals and objectives that God set—if it is not fulfilling God's heart desires—you must go back and cry out for the Lord to reveal where you have strayed and to lead you back to the place where He can work through you. We need to be sure that we are being fruitful and reaching and achieving God's targets; this will ensure that we are serving God's purposes and not living wasted lives.

▶ Exercise:

Today, read Genesis chapters 1-12. Be looking for

- God's situation analysis
- God's mission
- God's goals and objectives
- God's chosen vessel
- God's mandate to man

Be prepared to discuss these in your small group.

Time for Reflection:

What really strikes you about God's purposes? What adjustments do you need to make in your life so that you can join Him and cooperate with Him? ____________

What does God want you to do in response to this? ____________

As you pray your prayer target for this day/week, what are you feeling the Holy Spirit is saying or calling you to and what is the warfare coming against you? ____________

▸ Prayer Time:

Ask the Lord to create in you a heart that is yielded and willing to be a vessel He would choose to work through to accomplish His purposes. Allow Him to take you to deeper levels than you have gone before. This is the time, the hour when we pray into understanding the ways of God; ask Him to give you revelation and help you to understand His ways. Come to a deeper level of trust in Him.

Lesson 2.

Situation Analysis: God's Mission & Goals

When God looks at a situation, how does He analyze it? Look at Genesis 6:5-8: "The Lord saw how great man's wickedness on earth had become, and that every inclination of the thoughts of his heart was only evil all the time. And the Lord was grieved that he had made man on the earth, and his heart was filled with pain. So the Lord said, 'I will wipe mankind, whom I have created, from the face of the earth—men and animals, and creatures that move along the ground, and birds of the air—for I am grieved that I have made them.' But Noah found favor in the eyes of the Lord."

▸ **Exercise:**

Read Genesis 6:5-8 in the paragraph above.

What was the situation? ______________________________

____

____

What was God's mission? ______________________________

____

____

What was God's goal? ______________________________

____

____

God looked at the situation, He analyzed it, and He made a verdict. When God makes an analysis of a situation, He pronounces what He sees. It says in these scriptures that He was grieved; it grieved Him that He had even created man. And then He stated His mission: "I am going to bring destruction on the whole earth." What, then, is His goal? He wanted a completely new beginning. His next step was to choose a vessel through which He could accomplish that mission. And the Bible says that Noah found favor before God.

▸ **Exercise:**

Read Genesis 6:11-14 & 17-21

What was God's situation analysis? ______________________________

____

____

What was His mission? ____

____

____

What were His goals? ____

____

____

Who did He choose to help accomplish that mission? ________________

What was the commission He gave Noah? ____________________________

____

____

God saw that the ways of all the people on earth had become corrupt and that they had filled the earth with violence. He set a mission to cleanse the earth, to make a new beginning. He set goals to preserve a remnant from one family and a male and female from each species of animals, and to establish a covenant with Noah and his sons. God then commissioned Noah to build the ark; he was to keep alive the remnant of life that would be in the ark during the flooding that would destroy all other life on earth.

After the floods, God instructed Noah to come out of the ark and expanded his mission and mandate: "Then God blessed Noah and his sons, saying to them, 'Be fruitful and increase in number and fill the earth. The fear and dread of you will fall upon all the beasts of the earth and all the birds of the air, upon every creature that moves along the ground, and upon all the fish of the sea; they are given into your hands. Everything that lives and moves will be food for you. Just as I gave you the green plants, I now give you everything. But you must not eat meat that has its lifeblood still in it.'" (Genesis 9:1-4) When we are faithful with a little, God always gives more (Matthew 25:21).

God repeated the commission He gave Adam to Noah because He is committed to His work. Once God sets a mission, He is committed to fulfilling it; He doesn't change it or alter it.

▶ Exercise:

Read the story of Julio Ruibal on the next page.

What was Julio Ruibal's destiny and calling? ____________________________

____

____

Testimony: Julio Ruibal

Corruption was everywhere in Cali, Colombia, in the early 1990s. Drugs totally dominated the culture, murder occurred every day on the streets. The church, which was only a very small segment of society, was intimidated, not able to stand against this darkness. Any attempt of the government coming against the drugs and violence usually resulted in someone being killed. Any politician, judiciary, or police officer who rose up to fight against it would be murdered. God analyzed the situation and set a mission to raise up the churches in the land to stand against the darkness.

Julio Ruibal, a pastor in Cali, began to be burdened that this was a stirring of God. This was not the way things should be; there was a darkness that covered the land. God began to show him that this was a battle that not one pastor, not one church, not one denomination could win, that it would take the body of Christ. God showed Julio that the way to fulfill His mission was to bring unity between the churches and the pastors.

Julio Ruibal began to go about fulfilling this objective, calling the pastors to come together. He began to see how the pastors did not love each other; there was competition, jealousies, and disunity among them. He began to see that they would need to come together to pray and stand against the darkness. At times, he found it hard to stay united himself and wanted to break away from the group, but he couldn't get out from under God's instructions: "You don't have the right to be offended. You have to go back and humble yourself before the pastors, confess, and join in unity with them." The Lord even began to show him that the cost of seeing this kind of breakthrough may require his life. Julio prayed and came to a place of saying, "God, I'll lay down my life to see your purposes fulfilled."

The church of Cali began to unite in prayer. Their first all-night prayer vigil was held in the coliseum in March 1995; over 20,000 people attended. Miraculously, this was also the first weekend in history with no murder reported in Cali. Ten days later, one of the seven drug lords in Cali was killed in a military operation. Additional prayer vigils were held in the soccer stadium in August and November 1995, filling the 55,000-seat venue each time.

Shortly after the prayer nights began, the drug lords started coming down, one right after the other. The churches started to grow. Everything began to be affected: family life, the laws of the land, the spiritual climate. The clouds of darkness were being pushed back and the presence of God began to come to Cali and move among the people.

All this climaxed when Julio Ruibal was shot in the streets of Cali, Colombia, in December 1995. When the pastors came to his funeral, they began to break down and say, "We've got to come together." Inspired by the Holy Spirit, they made a covenant of unity with one another at Julio's funeral: *"We are one and we will let nothing divide us."* Even though they had already started to walk in unity, Julio's death sealed this in each of their hearts. The spiritual ground that Julio gained began to be released in the pastors' hearts in Cali, and the city has continued to experience increased unity, spiritual growth, transformation, and salvations.

What goals and objectives did God fulfill through Julio Ruibal? ____________
____
____

Did Julio Ruibal accomplish the mission God had set before him? Describe the fruit of Julio Ruibal's ministry: ____________________
____

▶ Exercise:

Today, read Genesis chapters 13-25. Be looking for

- God's situation analysis
- God's mission
- God's goals and objectives
- God's chosen vessel
- God's mandate to man

Be prepared to discuss these in your small group.

▶ Prayer Time:

Allow the Holy Spirit to show you any place in your heart that may be resistant to His work or ways. Remember the testimony of Julio Ruibal; ask the Lord if you would be willing to lay down your life to see His purposes advanced. Don't be afraid of the answer; remember that the Truth sets us free. Ask Him to lead you into a deeper willingness and desire to do His work, no matter what the cost.

Time for Reflection:

What really strikes you about God's purposes? What adjustments do you need to make in your life so that you can join Him and cooperate with Him? ____________
____
____
____
____
____
____
____
____
____

What does God want you to do in response to this? ____________
____
____
____
____
____
____
____
____
____
____
____

As you pray your prayer target for this day/week, what are you feeling the Holy Spirit is saying or calling you to and what is the warfare coming against you? ____________
____
____
____
____
____
____
____
____
____

Lesson 3.
Being Disqualified

God is committed to His mission. When we veer from His mission, not only will we not be fulfilling the desires of His heart, we can become disqualified from fulfilling our destiny.

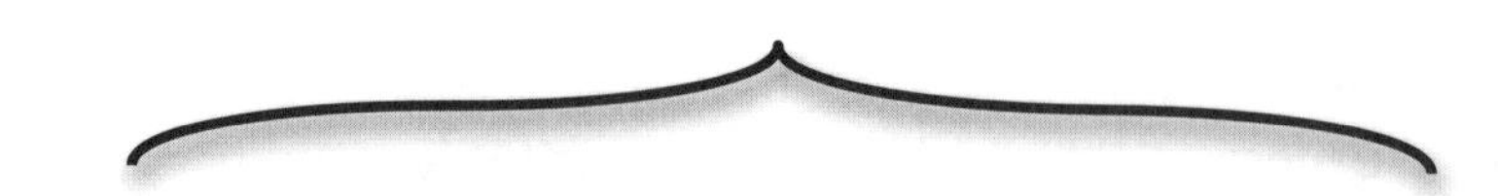

Becoming disqualified means that we have taken ourselves out of position to do ministry, to serve God. We are no longer available for God to use us to fulfill His purposes.

We are not standing in a position through which He can accomplish the work through us. Many times this occurs because we've left that place of surrender and trust, or we've begun to walk away from His instructions and promises, the things that He's given us to keep us on the path of fulfilling His mission.

Prayerfully go through today's lesson, seeking the Lord to reveal any self, sin, or worldliness that would take you out of position and keep you from the fullness of your destiny and fulfilling God's heart desires.

Disqualification

Beloved, we are living in a time when so many people who were called by God have strayed from their destiny. There are many leading churches and ministries, but they are no longer in position for God to be able to work through them. When we become disqualified, we may still be able to do a lot of work, but we are no longer doing God's work. God can no longer work through us to accomplish His purposes in mighty ways, as He did through Noah, Moses, Gideon, Paul, and so many others. We are no longer in position to fulfill God's heart desires in our generation.

In 2 Corinthians 13:5, Paul says to the Corinthians, "Examine yourselves to see whether you are in the faith; test yourselves." First of all, remember "faith comes by hearing, and hearing by the word of God" (Romans 10:17, NKJV). Paul was saying, "Examine yourselves. Are you are still standing in what you heard? Are you submitting to what God told you to do? Are

Testimony: Mark Daniel

At 16 years of age, God came and moved in a crusade in my town, and I saw God begin to awaken something in kids who were on the football team with me and in other students in the school. I began to hold meetings with about 100 students throughout the town, helping them draw closer to God and surrender themselves to Him.

At that age, I clearly knew that God had a calling on my life. Years later, while in college, I began really sensing God calling me to radically surrender and abandon myself to Him, and that this is what Christianity was meant to be. I had a burden to want to call people into this.

Seeing the need for an awakening, I would read the stories of revivalists and weep, longing for the church to be in that state, knowing that it would require the full surrender of my life to see this come about. I could feel the calling, and even see what God was revealing about the state of things around me.

I then went to seminary and got busy in ministry; I took my eyes off the Lord's calling and started to fulfill the expectations of people, the responsibilities and demands of my job as a pastor, and got lost. I was no longer about the call that God had given me.

In 1996, I was at a Promise Keepers event in Atlanta. Many clergy were there, crying out for the nation. I fell on the floor of the Georgia Dome, weeping and weeping for a long time because I had come to realize that I had spent the past 17 years not fulfilling my destiny and calling.

A year later, I saw a *Transformation* video in India, and again laid on the floor weeping because I was tapping into my calling and realized that I had not been about it. I spent the next few years being confronted that I wasn't walking in my calling and began to cry out to God because I didn't know how to come into position, how to fulfill my destiny; I didn't even know where to begin. And that's when God began to speak to me, drawing me back to the same objectives and instructions: "You must surrender everything to Me. It will require you giving up your life. Your life will no longer be yours; it will be Mine." He was drawing me back to that same surrender I had seen in my youth.

It was at that time that I began to say "yes" to that surrender and began to experience God leading me and shaping me into a vessel that He could use. That is when I met Pastor John Mulinde and we started to walk together, when God began to bring me into the nations to carry the message of set apart and surrender.

you still in the faith?" He goes on to say, "Test yourselves. Do you not realize that Christ Jesus is in you – unless, of course, you fail the test?" (2 Corinthians 13:5).

Many of us can remember when God commissioned us. We can clearly remember the words He spoke to us. He analyzed the situation and showed us the state of our nation, the state of the church, the lost souls all

across our country, or some other situation He wanted to change, and He began to say, "I want you to be involved in this work. I want to see these things begin to take place." But somewhere along the way, we began to get busy doing the work of ministry and drifted away from God's mission, His objectives, and allowing Him to work through us. That is where we can get in jeopardy of becoming disqualified. We are still doing ministry, but no longer doing the work God called us to. We are no longer about His mission; we are just running programs and operations.

Pastor Daniel's testimony shows that we can spend years not fulfilling the work that we've been given. In that place, we aren't even qualified or in position to fulfill or even clearly see the work that God has given us to do. This is a precarious place to stay because you don't know when you will be given another chance to see it again. It is also dangerous because the enemy can capture us in this place and pull us away from our destiny and calling.

▸ Pause for Reflection and Prayer:

Are you walking in what you heard from the Lord when He called you? If you don't see fruit of Christ Jesus working in you, you could have been pulled away from your destiny and calling. Spend a few minutes seeking the Lord for revelation and guidance. Journal what He shows you: _______

____

____

____

____

____

____

____

____

____

____

____

____

____

Biblical Example

The Bible is full of stories of people who drifted away from their destiny. One important example is the story of Elijah, who God used mightily to fulfill His purposes. The following narrative is from 1 Kings 17-19.

> All of Israel had begun to worship other gods. God's mission was to show them that He was the only true God and there was no other like Him, so He commissioned Elijah to stand against the false teachings and used him to shake their belief system.
>
> One of the first things Elijah did was to declare that there would be no rain: "As the Lord, the God of Israel, lives, whom I serve, there will be neither dew nor rain in the next few years except at my word" (1 Kings 17:1). In other words, "If you have other gods, let them change that prophecy." The rain did not come until it was clear to all the people that there was no other god; no one had the power to change the word of Elijah and bring rain.
>
> Elijah's commission was to lift up God; help Israel see that there is no other god. God promised Elijah He would be with him, and scripture shows that He was. Elijah confronted King Ahab and all the Israelites, saying, "How long will you waver between two opinions? If the Lord is God, follow him; but if Baal is God, follow him" (1 Kings 18:21). As long as Elijah was within the commission God had given him, God worked through him, protecting him and empowering him. You know the story of how Elijah mocked the prophets of Baal and won the contest (1Kings 18:18-40). Elijah showed that his God is the true God, then he killed all the prophets who were there. The Lord revealed through this that He was the only God, and afterward, Elijah went and prayed, and then it rained.
>
> Elijah obeyed and met the standards God had set for him until he heard that Jezebel was threatening to kill him, as he had killed the prophets of Baal. She threatened, "May the gods deal with me, be it ever so severely, if by this time tomorrow I do not make your life like one of them" (1 Kings 19:2). Jezebel was proclaiming that there was no difference between the prophets of Baal and Elijah, and she meant to prove it.
>
> How did Elijah respond to Jezebel's threats? He ran away. His very calling was being challenged. Jezebel was saying, "You are no different from these, and I'm going to prove that tomorrow." Elijah went into fear and ran for his life. He ran a day's journey into the desert, where an angel fed him and then took him on a 40-day journey to Mount Horeb (1 Kings 19:3-9).
>
> What did God say to Elijah while he was in a cave on that mountain? "What are you doing here, Elijah?" (1 Kings 19:9). Like we would do, Elijah tried to explain himself: "I have been very zealous for

the Lord God Almighty. The Israelites have rejected your covenant, broken down your altars, and put your prophets to death with the sword. I am the only one left, and now they are trying to kill me too" (1 Kings 19:10).

God told Elijah to go stand on the mountain and wait for His presence to pass by. But Elijah did not go. Powerful winds came, followed by an earthquake and fire. Elijah then heard a gentle whisper, so he moved to stand at the mouth of the cave. "Then a voice said to him, 'What are you doing here, Elijah?' He replied, "I have been very zealous for the Lord God Almighty. The Israelites have rejected your covenant, broken down your altars, and put your prophets to death with the sword. I am the only one left, and now they are trying to kill me too'" (1 Kings 19:11-14). He was in fear and his attitude was, "It's all about me now. You don't care!"

1 Kings 19:15-18 says, "The Lord said to him, 'Go back the way you came, and go to the Desert of Damascus. When you get there, anoint Hazael king over Aram. Also, anoint Jehu son of Nimshi king over Israel, and anoint Elisha son of Shaphat from Abel Meholah to succeed you as prophet. Jehu will put to death any who escape the sword of Hazael, and Elisha will put to death any who escape the sword of Jehu. Yet I reserve seven thousand in Israel—all whose knees have not bowed down to Baal and all whose mouths have not kissed him.'"

What was God saying to Elijah? "I have seven thousand In Israel you don't even know about who have never bowed down to Baal. Now you go and anoint Elisha to become a prophet in your place. Anoint him not to be a prophet in his own right, but to be a prophet in your place." Disqualification.

You can see that Elijah was disgruntled when he went to Elisha. He did not even tell him what God had said; he just threw his mantle on Elisha and walked away. Elisha, knowing that this meant God had called him into ministry, ran after Elijah, asking for time to say goodbye to his family. But Elijah, ever dejected, says, "Go back. What have I done to you?" Elisha goes home, finishes his business, then follows and serves the prophet (1 Kings 19:19-21).

Finally, on the day Elijah was to be taken up to heaven, he tells Elisha three times, "Stay here. I'm going over there." And every time, Elisha says, "I'm not leaving you. I'm going with you." You can tell that Elijah, who knows that something has been taken from him, is not happy, but Elisha is determined to not leave his side. After they cross the Jordan, Elijah asks Elisha, "What can I do for you before I am taken from you?" Elisha asks for a double anointing: "Let me inherit a double portion of your spirit." "You have asked a difficult thing," Elijah said, "yet if you see me when I am taken from you, it will be yours—otherwise not." And this is exactly what happened; Elisha saw Elijah taken up to heaven in a whirlwind and received the anointing he had asked for (2 Kings 2: 1-11).

This is a demonstration of how we can so easily get disqualified. We can't say that Elijah failed, but we can say that he lost his position and became disqualified.

Elijah is one of two men who made mistakes that cut their ministries short: the other is Moses. Moses was supposed to take the children of Israel to the Promised Land, but because of his failure, God said, ""Because you did not trust in me enough to honor me as holy in the sight of the Israelites, you will not bring this community into the land I give them" (Numbers 20:12). And he did not. Moses had become disqualified from doing the work the Lord had given him to do.

It's interesting to note that when Jesus was about to go through his Passion, He asked His disciples, "Sit here while I go over there and pray." "My soul is overwhelmed with sorrow to the point of death. Stay here and keep watch with me" (Matthew 26:36, 38). It's the first time Jesus ever asked anybody to stay with Him to pray. Before that, though, Elijah and Moses came to meet with Jesus on the Mount of Transfiguration. We don't know what they said to Him, but these are two men who God used mightily. Both of them exited their ministries prematurely. Perhaps they came to stand with Jesus and encouraged Him to not give up as He went through His darkest time.

How Do We Avoid Being Disqualified?

In Hebrews 10, Jesus says, "Sacrifice and burnt offerings you did not desire, but a body you prepared for me" (Hebrews 10:5). In other words, God gave Jesus a body that was prone to sin, that was human, and yet, He did not allow Jesus to offer Him burnt offerings or sin offerings. How did Jesus respond to this? "Here I am—it is written about me in the scroll—I have come to do your will, O God" (Hebrews 10:7). Jesus settled things right at the beginning. He declared He would do nothing but God's will, because that is what was written in the scrolls about Him.

Brethren, every one of us has a scroll written about us. It is God's blueprint for our lives. This is where the word "disqualification" becomes meaningful, because there is a blueprint. The blueprint won't be edited because you have deviated from the plans of God. No. When we change and leave the plans of God, we are no longer able to fulfill His work. We are no longer following the scroll, which was written before we were born.

You see this precept again and again in the Bible. Jeremiah, Samson, Cyrus, Jesus Christ—God talked about all of them before they were born. He says what they are going to do, what they will accomplish, what their ministries will bring to others. He does not look at their performance; He looks at His plan. He looks at the scroll.

If we would remind ourselves of this, we would tread softly. We would stop being swayed by everything that comes by and remember that He is the one who determines the exact places where we shall live and the times appointed for us. This means that if you and I are alive in this generation, it is by design. Our lives are supposed to be a certain way so that God can accomplish something through us in this generation.

If we are not the way He intended our lives to be, He can't work through whatever we offer Him, and therefore we will not see Him intervening in our generation. We will have lost our destiny.

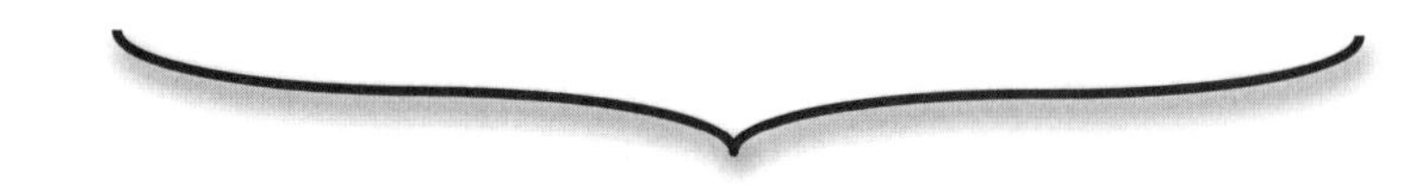

When we realize we have lost sight of His purposes and His call on our lives, we need to cry out to God and ask Him to bring us back into position to do His work.

Conclusion

We all receive commissioning and calling; God has created each of us with destiny and purpose, and involves us in His work. Instead of getting busy and distracted by the world and the things around us, we need to cry out for God to help us stay humble and focused on what He has asked us to do. And in those moments when we realize we have lost sight of His purposes and His call on our lives, we need to cry out to God and ask Him to bring us back into position to do His work.

▶ Pause for Prayer:

Ask God to remind you of the calling and commission that you've received. Ask Him to strip away any ways that you've compromised or mixed what He's asked of you with the ways of the world or your own thoughts, to show you any way you've lost sight of what He's asked. Begin to humble yourself and cry out, "God, I want to come back to the purity of what You have called me to do. I want to be standing in the position You have given me so that You can fulfill the work that You have required of me." Journal anything the Holy Spirit shows you: ______________________________

▸ Exercise:

Today, read Genesis chapters 26-38. Be looking for

- God's situation analysis
- God's mission
- God's goals and objectives
- God's chosen vessel
- God's mandate to man

Be prepared to discuss these in your small group.

Time for Reflection:

What really strikes you about God's purposes? What adjustments do you need to make in your life so that you can join Him and cooperate with Him? ______________________________

What does God want you to do in response to this? ______________________________

As you pray your prayer target for this day/week, what are you feeling the Holy Spirit is saying or calling you to and what is the warfare coming against you? ______________________________

Lesson 4.
God's Vessel

Destiny comes to you before you were born and is your divine identity.

Once God has analyzed a situation, established a mission, and set goals and objectives that will help fulfill that mission, He chooses a vessel through which He can work to meet those goals, thus accomplishing His mission. This releases the divine purpose—the destiny, or course of life that God ordained before time began. Destiny comes to you before you were born and is your divine identity. It is what is written about you in the scroll and includes calling, gifting, and molding.

An illustration of destiny is Jeremiah. God told Jeremiah, "Before I formed you in the womb I knew you, before you were born I set you apart; I appointed you as a prophet to the nations" (Jeremiah 1:5). God knew even before Jeremiah was born what his destiny would be, what God would call him to do in his generation. God had already predetermined Jeremiah's role, he already had a specific purpose for Jeremiah to fulfill: he was to be a prophet to the nations.

"Before I formed you in the womb I knew you, before you were born I set you apart; I appointed you as a prophet to the nations"
Jeremiah 1:5

Destiny

Destiny comes before we are born and involves calling, gifting, and molding. In other words, our destiny includes the purpose for which we were created. It is our DNA, our divine identity. It also includes the giftings, abilities, and talents that God gave us to be able to fulfill our calling. God also ordains situations in our lives that mold us, that strengthen our character, mature us, etc. These prepare us to do the works that we were created to do.

Destiny, calling, and gifting were all inside Moses even as he was a little boy floating in a basket in the river. God ordained that Moses would grow up in the Egyptian palace. This was a part of his molding; he was not intimidated by the Egyptian system the way the other Hebrews would have been. Going into the desert and being set apart by God, having an encounter with God at the burning bush, and then coming back to Egypt in the power of God were all part of one thing: Moses' destiny.

Calling is something you are born with; it has been inside of you even before you were in your mother's womb. God gives us our personality, qualities, and skills. He forms every part of us. This is our calling; it makes us who we are and helps us fulfill the purposes for which we were created.

We can use our calling to serve the world, but we will not be fulfilling the commission we were given. For example, Moses would have been a great leader whether He was obeying the Lord or doing something else because that is the way God made him; it is part of his calling. But God had a destiny for Moses and told him, "So now, go. I am sending you to Pharaoh to bring my people the Israelites out of Egypt" (Exodus 3:10).

When God chooses a vessel to use for His work, He ordains a process of bringing that vessel into fulfillment (molding). For example, Hebrews 5:7-8 says that during His days on earth, Jesus prayed with loud groanings and tears to His father, who could have saved Him from death. Although he was the Son of God, Jesus learned obedience through the things he suffered. And after he had been perfected, he became the Savior of all who obey Him. So we can see that even Christ had to go through a molding process; there are things that the Father ordained for Him to suffer on earth in order to come to the fullness of being the Savior of all creation.

Jesus was the Lamb of God before the creation of the earth; that was His destiny. But He received his commissioning when the Father sent Him out: "For God so loved the world that he gave his one and only Son" (John 3:16). In Hebrews 10:5-9, when Jesus is speaking of his commissioning, he says, "You did not want animal sacrifices or sin offerings. But you have given me a body to offer. You were not pleased with burnt offerings or other offerings for sin. Then I said, 'Look, I have come to do your will, O God—as is written about me in the Scriptures'" (NLT). At His commissioning, it was clear that Jesus was not to revert to the offerings and sacrifices and practices of atonement described in the Old Testament; yet, he had to be without sin, so He made a resolution and said, "I will come forth to do the will of God, even as it is written about Me."

You can see that when the Father chose who to send to save the world, he determined His destiny. God describes the destiny of the Messiah

Testimony: East African Revival

The East African Revival, which spread throughout the region and had a strong impact on the nations of Congo, Rwanda, Kenya, and Uganda, probably started in June or July of 1929 under a beautiful acacia tree on Ndera Hill, ten miles from Rwanda's capital, Kigali. A group of four men were gathered under that tree: three Africans (Simeoni Nsibambi, Blasio Kigozi, and Yosiya Kinuka) and an English missionary doctor (Joe Church), physically and spiritually exhausted. A devastating famine had swept Rwanda and thousands had died. The famine seemed to be symptomatic of a famine of the Spirit, for nominal Christianity characterized the great majority of the churches.

Nothing spectacular happened to begin with. Simeoni and Joe sat and read the Bible together for three days and caught a new vision of the person of Jesus Christ. They sensed a blessing – a liberation – and began to share what they were learning. There were things in their lives that needed putting right. Before long, others were aware that something had happened to Simeoni and Joe.

Yosiya Kinuka caught the vision and was transformed overnight into a passionate evangelist. Blasio Kigozi became a flame that blazed with incredible fervor until his premature death from fever, but he left an indelible mark on the church of Uganda.

Then in 1932, William Nagenda was converted. Irritated by the Gospel songs he heard outside his government offices in Entebbe, he burst open the door, and found Simeoni and some others. "Why are you carrying on like this?" he asked. "Ah," came the enigmatic reply, "We only wish you knew!" Nagenda strode away angrily, but the words challenged his thinking, and at midnight he turned in prayer and faith to Christ. A new evangelist had been born, whose voice was to be heard across Africa and all over the world.

William Nagenda was to be joined by Festo Kivengere. They were surely among the most effective evangelists that there have ever been. Others came into the picture, including Erica Sabiti, who was to become Uganda's first and saintly African archbishop.

Through song and personal testimony, through bold preaching and public witness - and often in the face of strong opposition and downright hostility – the East African church became transformed, There was no organization; all was spontaneous and of the Spirit. Unbelievers in the hills would be convicted of their sins in the middle of the night, and would come running to the church. People who were deep in witchcraft and idol worship turned to worship the God of heaven. Old feuds were mended and there was restitution of stolen property. People from the western region of Uganda began to give their children names in connection with God, which is ongoing even today. The church became powerful, and people became followers of Christ by the thousands.

Marked features of the Revival were that it stayed within the established churches; that those caught up in it were unashamed and bold in their witness; that it was anchored in the central truths of the Gospel; and that it had an ethical dimension: sin mattered, repentance was vital, holiness was imperative, and Christians were to walk in the light with one another, with honesty.

throughout the entire Old Testament. He talks about "My Spirit shall be upon Him." "My covenant will be with Him." "He will not judge by sight." "He will not do this or that." Isaiah and all the others prophets describe the Messiah, but all they are really doing is describing His destiny, calling, gifting, and molding.

Then, when the fullness of time came for Him to be commissioned, Jesus' destiny was fulfilled by His death. He said, "not as I will, but as you will" (Matthew 26:39).

Jesus was given a commissioning, He had a covenant relationship with the Father, He had instructions, promises, and the anointing and grace to do the work.

God will not ask you to do something He has not already prepared you for.

He has already equipped you; it's inside you. There is an incorruptible seed inside there, and just as a seed looks small but has the potential to produce a tree and fruit and many other things, so is the calling inside of you. It has the potential; we only have to put faith and trust in the Lord that He has already put those things inside us.

We can use our calling – what God put inside of us when we were created – in many various ways, but unless we are using it to fulfill the commission we have been given, our lives will not be fulfilled and we risk being disqualified and bearing little fruit for the Lord. We will not be serving Him or fulfilling His purposes, which is a fearful thing to do.

Unless we are using it to fulfill the commission we have been given, our lives will not be fulfilled and we risk being disqualified and bearing little fruit for the Lord.

▸ Exercise:

Read Matthew 25:14-30. What happens to those who do not use what God gave them to fulfill His purposes? ______________________

____

____

____

Vessels That God Can Use to Do His Work

Read the testimony about the East African Revival, then review the testimonies we read this week about George Mueller and Julio Ruibal. All of these men, through their yieldedness to God, fulfilled the mission that He gave them. George Mueller's faith showed that God is real and powerful, that He is mindful of His people, and that He answers prayer. People in the United Kingdom began once again to have faith, and this spread to Europe and other continents of the world. Julio Ruibal's desire to see God's will done in Cali, Colombia, and his willingness to die for the cause God laid on his heart opened the door for a strong bond of unity among the pastors and churches in Cali. The church went from being small, powerless, and insignificant to vibrant and full of life. Thousands of people have come to the Lord in the years since Julio's death. The East African Revival affected many nations in Africa and spread throughout other continents of the world. Ministries in these nations, once recipients of missionaries from the West, are now beginning to raise up and train missionaries that are being sent out all over the world. The East African Revival laid a foundation of faith that continues to impact nations all around the world.

These few testimonies show that when we give ourselves fully to God, He can work through us to fulfill the purposes for which we were created.

These men took God's heart desires as their own heart desires; their focus became fulfilling God's purposes; they took the burdens of His heart as their own burdens. Because they allowed God to work through them, they bore fruit—lasting fruit—that they could have never produced on their own, and nations were touched by their surrender to the Lord.

Similarly, when we yield our lives fully to the Lord and allow Him to work in and through us, we will have the blessing of Him doing things through us that we could never do on our own. We will bear more fruit than we could have ever imagined possible; fruit that will have a lasting impact on all those around us.

Exercise:

Today, read Genesis chapters 39-50. Be looking for

- God's situation analysis
- God's mission
- God's goals and objectives
- God's chosen vessel
- God's mandate to man

Be prepared to discuss these in your small group.

Time for Reflection:

What really strikes you about God's purposes? What adjustments do you need to make in your life so that you can join Him and cooperate with Him? ______________

What does God want you to do in response to this? ______________

As you pray your prayer target for this day/week, what are you feeling the Holy Spirit is saying or calling you to and what is the warfare coming against you? ______________

Prayer Time:

Spend time today praising and thanking the Lord that He would include us in His work. Thank Him for all the things He's revealed to you these past few weeks; praise Him for His goodness, faithfulness, and mercy. Thank Him for His correction and discipline. Spend time adoring Him and speaking out how much you love Him, all the things about Him that you treasure, how you are so thankful that He is your God and you are His child. Bless the name of the Lord.

Notes

Week 5.

God's Mandate

Last week we learned the pattern by which God works. He analyzes a situation, sets a mission, determines goals and objectives, chooses a vessel through which He will accomplish His work, and then gives a mandate to this vessel. There are six components to this mandate:

1. Commissioning
2. Catching the vision of God's heart
3. Covenantal position
4. Commandments and instructions
5. Gifts and promises
6. Grace and anointing to do the work

GOAL OF THE WEEK:

This week's lesson is the centerpiece of our whole study. We want to be able to fully grasp:

1. What is the mandate God has given us?

2. How can we begin to pray into this mandate so that it becomes written on our hearts and we are walking it out?

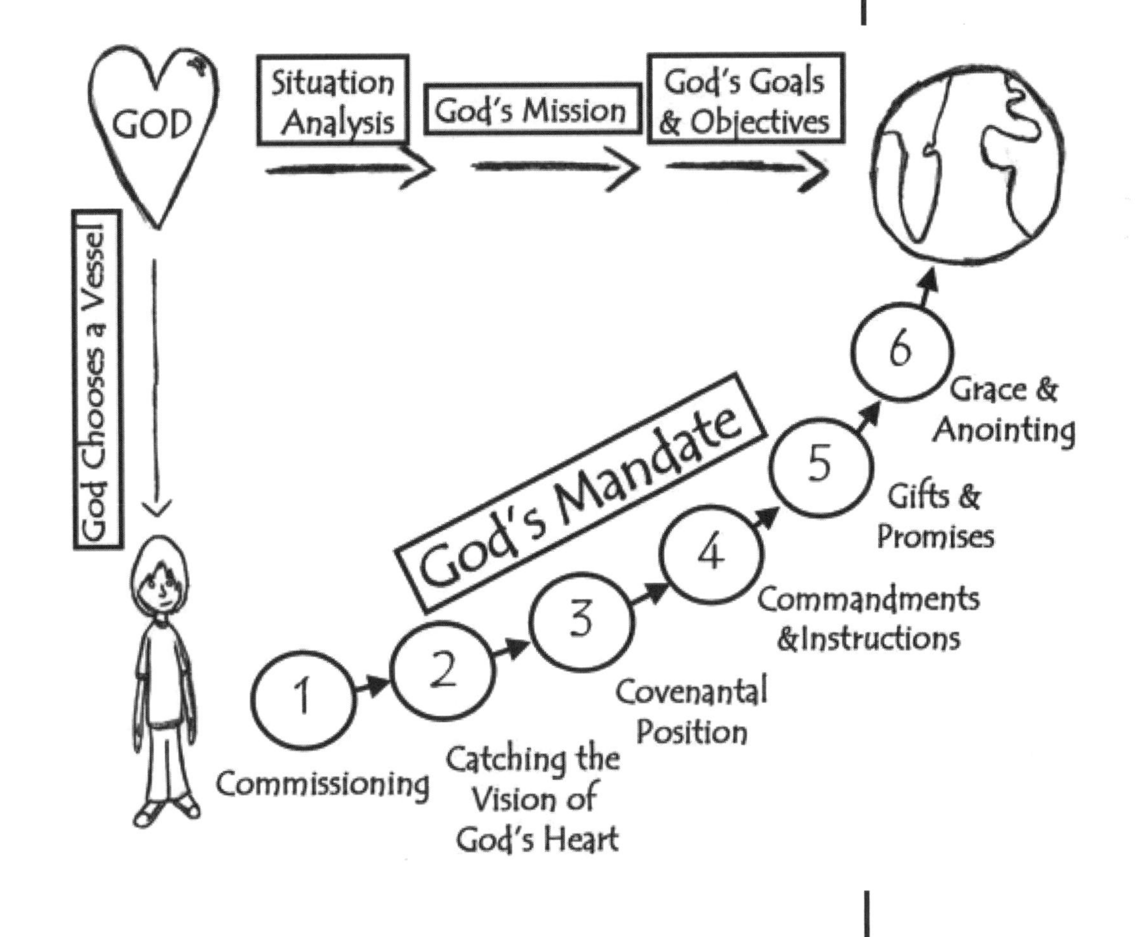

The **mandate** is what God gives us so we can fulfill His mission.

"Coming into position" is praying into the six components of mandate, beginning to hold them more deeply by faith and submitting our lives to them so that they are becoming more profound and solid in our lives.

We are going to be talking about coming into position throughout this workbook. What is meant by "coming into position" is that we are praying into these six components, beginning to hold them more deeply by faith and submitting our lives to them, and they are becoming more profound and solid in our lives.

The mandate is what God gives us so we can fulfill His mission. As He builds these six components into our lives, and as we continue to go deeper in our faith and submission to them, God is able to begin to fulfill His work through us. He will begin to give us the insight, understanding, and power we need to accomplish the work. When we begin to lose standing or depth in this position, our ability to carry out His purposes begins to diminish and we find ourselves shrinking back into running programs and doing good activities, unable to touch the power, wisdom, or insight needed to fulfill the purposes of God. It is therefore vital that we hold every single one of these six things deep within our hearts.

Prayer targets for week 5:

Pray into the six components of mandate. See more and more clearly each component, and come more deeply into the faith and submission to the fullness of God's mandate over your life.

Audio/video link for week 5:

http://worldtrumpet.org/awakening-the-church (week 5)

Lesson 1.

God's Mandate to Man: Commissioning

When God chooses a man or woman to join Him in His work, He also releases a mandate over them. The mandate includes the degree of authority and scope of the work that God has given to them.

God gives different mandates to different people. Some people's mandates are bigger than others. The bigger the mandate, the more people it's going to involve. It's also going to involve more ministries and gifts, as well as greater responsibility of leadership.

Some people's mandates are geographical, perhaps over a geographical territory. That is the territory in which your authority is released; if you go to another territory, you may find that you are completely without any impact because your mandate from the Lord does not stretch to that territory.

Some people's mandates are social, over a particular social group or a particular demographic group. And some people's mandate is generational. It stretches over several generations. Even after they have died and left this world, their mandate goes on, which means that there is an interest in God's heart to know who is succeeding the person to whom He has given this mandate.

We need to understand our mandate not only as individuals, but also within the concept of a corporate mandate of what God is doing in our generation. God always does things in the context of the bigger picture of the mission He has set and the goals and objectives He has established. For example, in the time of Moses, God analyzed the situation and saw what was going on with His people. He set the mission that He would deliver them from Egypt and raise them up to be His nation, and then He commissioned Moses and told Him to "bring my people to the mountain that they may worship me" (Exodus 3:7-12). An additional part of the mandate was that Moses was to take the Hebrews into the Promised Land.

This was the mandate that God gave to Moses, but there were others under this larger mandate who each had their own personal mandate. Joshua was called to be Moses' armor bearer, Aaron was called to be a

Testimony: John Mulinde

From the moment I got saved, I knew deep in my heart that God was calling me to preach the gospel. I don't know how, but I knew that I was going to travel the nations for His name.

I struggled for about 6 months trying to find what God was calling me to do. I asked my pastor to pray with me for direction. The more I prayed with the pastor, the more involved I got in the work. I also began fasting one week a month. We would stay in the church during the week of fasting and be in the word of God; it became life to me – I loved it.

Then God began to give me requirements and instructions: "I want you to live by faith. I want you to believe me with your whole heart." I didn't really understand Him. I didn't know if He was asking me to leave my job; all I really knew was that I wasn't to trust in anything else but Him.

During this time, I contracted malaria. Since I was living "by faith," I determined to not see a doctor or take any medication. It came to the point where I couldn't walk; I couldn't eat and I didn't want to drink anything. I was wasting away and ƒd to refuse medical treatment.

But God is good, even when we are immature. The night when I was at my worst, the Lord touched me and completely healed me. It happened in a dream. I had one dream three times, and in that dream I saw the Day had come, the Lord had come back; the sky had opened and I saw Him coming. People were running everywhere; many Christians and even some pastors were running away. The whole world was full of screaming and lots of sounds. I was trembling but I didn't know what to do.

And then I heard the Lord singing, and the song was very sorrowful. I can still hear it in my spirit. I can sing it even today. And in that song He was singing, "Where are My people? Where are they who are called by My name? Where are they who confessed knowing Me? They have fled because they took My Word lightly." And He was crying.

I had that dream three times; during the third time I was completely healed. That dream didn't concern my sickness at all, but what I didn't know at the time was that it concerned my destiny and God's mandate for my life, my ministry, what God would send me to go and do later on.

I was so strengthened in my faith; I even determined that I would never take medicine again because my Savior is my healer and He told me to live by faith. A few months later, He again spoke to me in a dream: "I want to prepare you for the work I have for you. For a time, I want you do nothing else but focus on three things: read My word, and engage yourself in prayer and in worship; that is how I want you to spend your time. I'm going to add a team to you. Everything I give you, give it to them. I want you to fellowship together in My word, because I am preparing you for a big work."

Eight months later, I had a supernatural visitation from Him during which He just laid my life before me. He showed me that I had started well when I got saved – all I wanted was Him – but as I walked I began to idolize other things and to take Him lightly. And now I was living two lives: an outward life that looked perfect to everybody and an inward life that was not acceptable to my Father. He told me, "I weighed you from the beginning to the end; your life is not acceptable to Me."

He led me through a process of renewal and total surrender to Him, and then He gave me the commissioning. He said, "I appear to you that I may send you to My church in the nations, to go and blow the trumpet and prepare them for My coming. I am coming very soon [the season of time called the Day of the Lord] but the church is not ready, and if they don't prepare they will be swept by the storms and traps of the last days.'" He told me to have faith and promised to be with me everywhere I went.

It was at that time that He said to me, "I've always told you to live by faith, but until now you have never accepted it," and I thought, "What does that mean? I've been living by faith; I left my job, I have no salary, I don't go to doctors, I am not dependent on anyone else." My understanding of faith was so limited. He took me back to the scriptures and said, "Faith comes by hearing, and hearing by the Word of God. I want you to take My Word as it is. Don't follow after teachers and preachers. Go back to My Word; I will teach you My ways."

The Lord said to me, "If you believe in Me, you will give Me your life and I will give you My life. Your life is no longer yours, it's Mine." This is also what the word says. When you come into Christ Jesus you become a new creature; the old has passed away, behold all things are new. You take on a new character, the life of Christ. And you need to study that life. Live for that life. Do the things that life is supposed to do. Pursue the mission that life is supposed to pursue.

"Give me your life" was the first requirement He asked of me. Later on, He said, "You can't do work for Me, you can only position yourself for Me to work through you." And our team started to seek God to find out how to position ourselves. "Give me your lives. Your life is no longer yours, it is Mine. You cannot live for any other reason in this world but the purposes My life came to accomplish. And because you are no longer your own, you've got to live by My standard, which is love. You've got to love people because I love them; not because they are good, but because I love them and I died for them."

"You can't do work for Me, you can only position yourself for Me to work through you."

priest in the community, Miriam was called to be a prophetess, others were called to be worshipers, judges, soldiers, craftsmen, laborers, and many other things; all of these people were part of the work God was doing and came under the larger mandate God gave to Moses.

We need to look at the mandate not only in individual terms, but also realize that we are all part of something bigger.

Refer back to Pastor Mark Daniel's testimony in lesson 3 of last week's study. When Pastor John Mulinde and Pastor Mark met, they were oceans apart in their walks. But God had put that calling and desire on Pastor Mark's life to abandon and surrender himself fully to the Lord, to set Himself apart, and to see the church awakened. When God caused their paths to cross, He was beginning to bring Pastor Mark up under Pastor John and into the larger mandate of what God is doing in this day and time. The mandate given to Pastor Mark, although it was for him individually, came up under the corporate mandate that the Lord had given to Pastor John.

It is this bonding of heart and purpose that the Lord uses to complete the works that He is doing in our time. That is why even as WTM team members travel throughout the nations, other people have already heard the call and they begin to come up under the larger mandate of the Lord. God is calling others under the mandate to fulfill the larger work that He is doing.

The Components of the Mandate God Gives

When we talk about mandate, we need to include a number of things:

1. **Commissioning:** Commissioning is the sending out of the Lord. It is Him speaking to you and saying, "I want you to go and do this."
2. **Catching the vision of God's heart:** The ability to see into God's heart; to see the realities of today, the ideal that God desires, and the process by which He plans to move from the reality of today to the ideal desires of His heart.
3. **Covenantal position:** Covenantal position is the spiritual position and attitude you are to be in so that God can do His work in and through you to fulfill His heart's desires. Simply stated, covenantal position is standing in the place of surrender and trust in the Lord; we trust Him, yield our will to Him, and obey the instructions and

direction He's given us. There will be different implications for each of our lives, but that position begins to become very clear as we seek to stand strongly with the Lord.

4. **Commandments and instructions:** God gives commandments, instructions, and requirements, which are intended to keep us in our covenantal position. These may seem hard and difficult to fulfill, but they are for our security and protection.
5. **Gifts and promises:** God gives us gifts and promises to fulfill His work. As we join Him in His work and come into our covenantal position, God will begin to give us promises of things He will accomplish. These are the things you hold up in the times of battle; you hold onto them as you seek to firmly hold onto the mandate that God has given you.
6. **Grace and anointing to do the work:** To fulfill the work of God, there are things that cannot be accomplished in our own power. Like Moses' Red Sea, we will find ourselves facing impossible situations. In such seemingly hopeless circumstances, we will stand and count on God's grace to be sufficient to see us through, and His anointing to be able to accomplish what our human effort is unable to accomplish.

God's Mandate — Component 1: Commissioning

The words that God uses to send you comprise His commissioning to you. When He speaks to you and says, "I want you to go and do this," that's the commissioning. He says, "Go and do." The commissioning is vital to the mandate as it defines the course that you are to be on. The instructions to "go and do" provide the roadmap and details of the work the Lord is inviting you to take part in.

▶ Exercise:

Read the following scriptures. What is the commission God gave to each of these men?

Judges 6:11-16: ____

____

____

Ezekiel 1-10: ____

____

____

Jonah 1:1-3, 1-5: ______________________________

____

____

Matthew 4:19: ______________________________

____

____

Acts 26:12-18: ______________________________

____

____

God told Gideon to "Go... and save Israel out of Midian's hand." He sent Ezekiel to the Israelites to speak His words to them. He told Jonah, "Go to the great city of Nineveh and preach against it." Jesus said to Peter, "Come, and I will make you fishers of men," and Paul was told, "I am sending you to them [the Gentiles] to open their eyes and turn them from darkness to light, and from the power of Satan to God."

When God commissions someone, He is sending them into action. He has analyzed the situation and determined a mission; He has work that He is doing and He invites a vessel to become a part of it. He then tells them, "Go; begin to do this."

▶ **Exercise:**

Look personally at yourself. Can you recall when God commissioned you? Is it still visible or has it faded and become foggy through the passing of time? ______________________________

____

____

When God first calls you or when you renew your covenant with Him, He also begins to call you into His purposes.

What is your commission? ______________________________

____

____

Are you fulfilling your commission? (circle one)

1 = Not at all
2 = I have lost sight of my commission
3 = I remember my commission and am doing a little, but am distracted
4 = I am seeking to get back in position
5 = I am fulfilling His mission

How does God want you to respond to the answers you gave above? ______

____

____

It is an honor to be called by the Lord to be involved in His work, but we sometimes find that we have strayed off course. When we test ourselves and find that we are standing in position and fulfilling the work He has given us to do—that we are on course—we can be thankful and praise Him for the grace that He has given us to fulfill His heart's desires. At those times, though, when we realize we are not fulfilling our commission—that we are off course—we must begin the process of humbling ourselves, repenting, and asking the Lord to restore us to that position where He can once again work through us to accomplish His purposes.

The Choices We Face

It is so easy to just go with the flow and busyness of life and allow God's calling to fade into the background. We dabble in doing ministry and serving God, but we never truly give our whole lives and heart to fulfilling what He called us to. We really need to come to the place where we decide whether our lives will be lives for His purposes and not this world's. Without that kind of definitive decision, we find ourselves beginning to drift off and never being able to stay about His commissioning.

Therefore, there are choices that we need to make: will we really follow the ways of God, taking up our mandate and walking out our commission, or will we walk in the ways of the world, jeopardizing our destiny and not fulfilling God's heart desires in our generation?

The way of the Lord is His pre-ordained course for you, where He molds and shapes us, and it begins to raise us up to the vessel that He can work through. The ways of man is the natural human tendency, bound by the world system. If we do not go the Lord's way, we put ourselves in a position where we are weakened and can fall prey to the traps and schemes in this world, never to be able to rise up to fulfill His call, which may limit or even nullify fulfilling God's purposes in our lives.

Many times we acknowledge God's call and commissioning on our lives, but we never make the choice to give our lives fully to that.

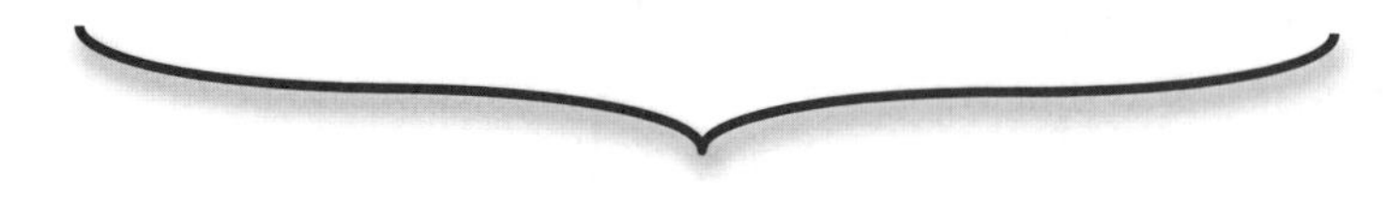

▶ **Exercise:**

Read the following scriptures, then describe the choices each man made and the results of that choice.

1 Samuel 15:1-29 (King Saul): ______________________________

____

____

1 Chronicles 17:4-14, Acts 13:22 (David): ______________________________

____

____

1 Kings 9:3-9, 11:6-11 (Solomon): ______________________________

____

____

Acts 9:1-22 (Paul): ______________________________

____

____

There are many examples of both of these choices in the Bible. Abraham, David, Daniel, Ezekiel, Peter, Paul, and so many others, chose a course of life that would allow God to work through them and thus fulfill the destiny for which they were created. Adam, Samson, King Saul, Solomon, Jeroboam, and others, however, chose a different course and thus failed to fulfill God's heart desires in their lifetime. These men did not just make one mistake; through the choices they made, they veered from the mission God gave them and so were unable to fulfill the purposes for which they were created.

The Lord gave David and Solomon specific instructions and requirements; He was saying, "I will fulfill the mandate through you as you walk in this way." Although David's life wasn't perfect, he did walk in the ways the Lord instructed him and God fulfilled His purposes through him. Solomon was given the same instructions and requirements but did not follow them; therefore, destiny was taken away from him and he was unable to fulfill the mandate God had given him.

Samson is also a good example of someone who never made the firm choice to give His whole heart to the mandate. He was commissioned to deliver Israel from the Philistines and was called to be a Nazarite, someone who is set apart for God to fulfill a specific purpose in his time (Judges 13:1-7). Samson had a choice: walk in the Nazarite walk or walk in the ways of men; it is clear which choice he made. God could have worked through Samson in much more powerful ways, but Samson's choices pulled him away from his mandate and limited the work that God could do through him.

The Lord gives all of us instructions and requirements. He says, "You must walk this way." The choices we make will determine whether we are able to fulfill or lose the mandate for which He created us. We hold onto the promises He's given us, believing the things He's called us into, standing in the position of trust and abandonment to Him—this is what will keep us on the course of fulfilling the mandate to which He has called us.

Conclusion

We encourage everyone taking this study to pray into the mandate from this day forward. The first reason is that our flesh begins to pull us away and we begin to live as normal human beings rather than as servants of the Most High God who have purpose and destiny to our lives. Secondly, we have an enemy who is constantly trying to attack our faith and to distract us and knock us off course. That is when we can begin to make choices that take us step by step, further and further away from the very purposes for which God has called us unto Himself, and therefore we are not fulfilling the mandate He's given us.

As we give our lives to God, He will fulfill His mandate in our lives and, like Paul, we will be able to say, "I have fought the good fight, I have finished the race, I have kept the faith. Now there is in store for me the crown of righteousness, which the Lord, the righteous Judge, will award to me on that day—and not only to me, but also to all who have longed for his appearing" (2 Timothy 4:7-8).

Time for Reflection:

What is the most meaningful statement or scripture you read today? ______________________________

What does God want you to do in response to this? ______________________________

As you pray your prayer target for this day/week, what are you feeling the Holy Spirit is saying or calling you to and what is the warfare coming against you? ______________________________

▶ **Prayer Time:**

Pray into the commissioning that you have been given. Ask the Holy Spirit to remind you what the Lord may have showed you in the past, ask Him to restore you to that place, seek Him for direction about how He desires for you to fulfill the commission you have been given, and ask Him to show you how to take hold of the commission and walk it out.

Lesson 2.

God's Mandate to Man: Catching the Vision of God's Heart

After God analyzes a situation, sets a mission for Himself, establishes goals and objectives, then chooses a vessel through which to work, He gives that vessel a mandate. What are the parts of the mandate? (Fill in the blanks on the drawing below.)

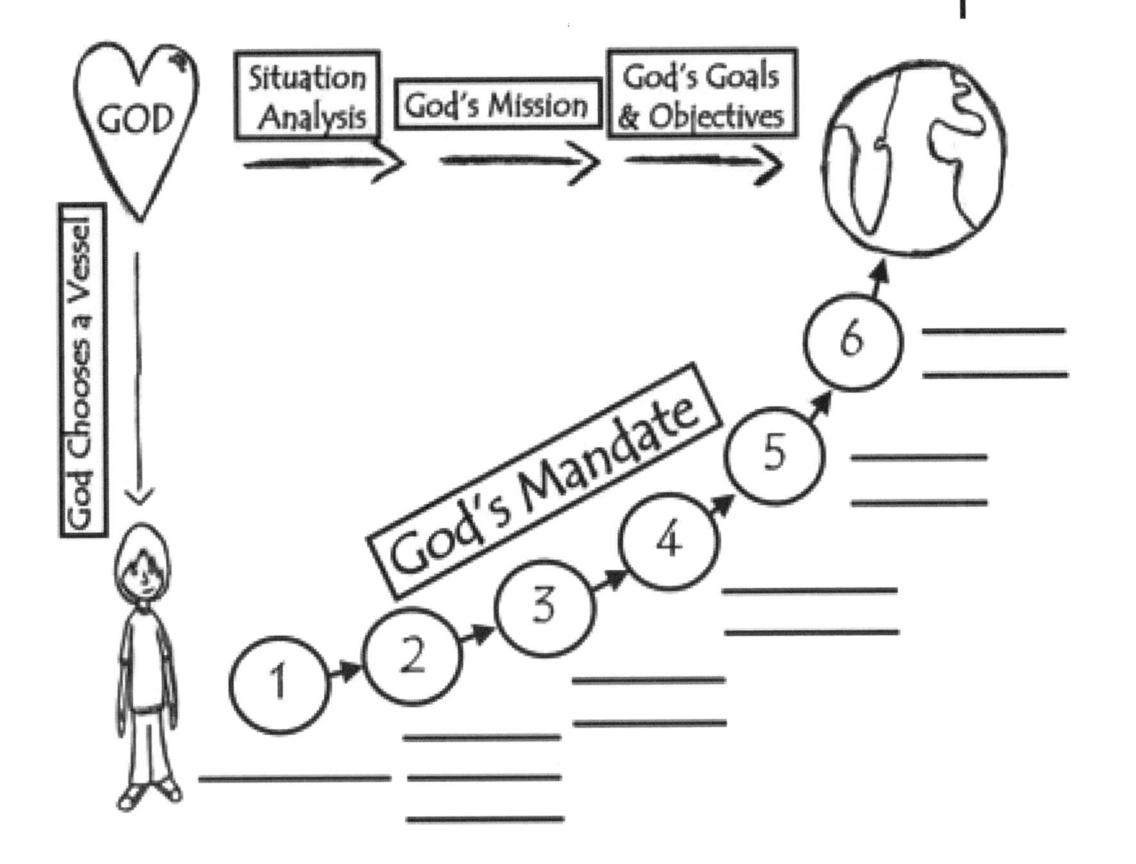

God's Mandate – Component 2: Catching the Vision of God's Heart

The second component of mandate is catching the vision of God's heart. We define this as the ability, by God's grace, to see into His heart. That is, to understand what God sees in the reality of today; what He desires in His ideal, perfect picture; and what He sees as the process needed to bring about this ideal.

Seeing things from God's perspective will give us clarity regarding the vision God has set and the goals and objectives He has established. This clarity helps us remain focused on the work He has called us to do, but more importantly, helps ensure that we are fulfilling the desires of His heart. Catching God's vision will give us a deeper hunger and desire for the things of God, and a deep stirring to join Him in His work and to live our lives for only one reason: to see His purposes fulfilled in all the earth. We will begin to live for God and His greater purposes rather than just for ourselves and our own ministry. We begin to see *His* purposes and they are far greater than anything we've ever carried before.

To do the works that God requires of us, it is vital to grasp the intentions of God's heart and take hold of the fullness of the mandate He has given us. The more fully we give ourselves to fulfilling the desires of God's heart and the more we pray into the position of His mandate, the more our understanding will begin to expand. We will then begin to have God's vision of the mission that He is on and a much fuller picture of the work that God is calling us into.

Many times, we want to rush into the action that we see. We don't take the time to connect deeply with God's heart, so we begin to get a more shallower view of things. To really pray and connect with God's heart is important; otherwise, you can slide back into just doing good activities. In fact, there are many times that we have encouraged ourselves to stop and seek the Lord to help us connect into His vision afresh. We do this because we know that if we don't, we just begin to drift off the course that the Lord has given us.

The Apostle Paul

The apostle Paul is someone who had captured God's vision. One of his greatest desires was to please the Father, to fulfill the purpose for which he had been created and the desires of God's heart. His commission is clear.

▶ **Exercise:**

Read Acts 26:15-18.

What was Paul's commission? ____________________

____

____

What are some of the goals and promises that the Lord gave him? ____________________

____

____

Paul had received a very clear commissioning from the Lord: "I have appeared to you to appoint you as a servant and as a witness of what you have seen of me and what I will show you." The commissioning came with goals and objectives (to open eyes, to turn people from darkness to light, from the power of Satan to God, so they may receive forgiveness of sins and a place in heaven) as well as promises (God would protect him from the Jews and the Gentiles). But his epistle to the Philippians shows us that the deepest driving force of Paul's life was not the commissioning he had been given.

Read Philippians 3:7-14. What does Paul say that indicates there was something deeper that drove him than just his commission? ____________

____

____

In the third chapter of Philippians, Paul says that he could boast about all kinds of things. He was a Hebrew of Hebrews, was circumcised on the eighth day, and blameless according to the law. He gave up everything to win Christ, to "be found with a righteousness that is not mine by the law but which is of God by the faith of Christ." Paul sought to know Christ at the deepest levels, "to know the power of His resurrection and the fellowship of His suffering and be conformed to His image even in death. Finally, he says, "I am not saying I am perfected already, but forgetting what is behind me, I reach out for that which is ahead. I want to lay hold of that for which He laid hold of me."

Paul could have very easily taken hold of the mission God gave him and run off to do a lot of work. But Philippians shows us that Paul was seeking something far deeper than just going to preach the gospel, more than just seeing people saved and entering into the kingdom. Paul realized that there is more than just coming to Christ; that even when we come to Christ, there is a quality of life, a righteousness that is not our own, but that comes from Him.

How do we get this deeper life in Christ? Paul says we attain it by forsaking everything else and coming into the fullness of His power and the fellowship of His suffering. This is really the set apart life; dying to self so that we may live for Christ. Paul had caught the vision of God's heart.

Even though Paul could have boasted about the fruit that he bore for the Lord, the churches that he established, the lives that he saved, or the way the Lord used him to spread the truth throughout the nations, he kept his focus on something even bigger.

▶ **Exercise:**

There was something that burned in Paul's heart even more. What was it? (see Philippians 3:12): ____

____

____

Paul knew that there was something in God's heart that caused Him to lay hold of Paul; there was a bigger purpose and vision that God was allowing him to take part in. "I want to lay hold of that."

If we allow our hearts to connect with what Paul is saying, we will realize that it is not just pursuing good works that fulfills the mandate God gives us; it is catching the vision of God's heart. It is not enough to just fulfill the small role in the mission that he has given us; we must see things from God's perspective and join Him in His desire to see the fullness of this greater vision.

Ministry is ____.
(*see* week 2, lesson 4)

Ministry is fulfilling the desires of God's heart; let us then seek the Lord for His perspective, to lay hold of that for which He took hold of us.

A key to catching the vision of God's heart is to see what He has been doing throughout the eras.

When you look beyond the commissioning or calling that God has given you—not just at the work that He's given you to do—and you grasp God's vision, the bigger picture of what His mission has been throughout the eras, you will begin to see where things are in the fulfillment of His heart's desire. You can see what He created them for, what purposes He intended them to fulfill, and then you can see clearly what is coming next. This begins to give a backdrop to the work that He's called you to do and to cause you to connect with His heart.

Looking at the Times in Which We Live From God's Perspective. In previous lessons, we have studied the different eras of time and what God's intention was in each one. The eras of time all become meaningful if we keep them in light of God's heart's desire, and understanding them is absolutely essential in order to capture God's heart and what He is doing in our time. God wanted all creation to bring out His glory, to reveal the fullness of who He is.

Let us remember that God wanted all creation to bring out His glory and bring out the fullness of who He is, and He wanted man to preside over and help all of creation come into its destiny. God has never changed the mission He set out to accomplish from the beginning of time.

The failure of man from the time of Adam to the tower of Babel caused God to decide to raise a nation for Himself. He wanted to set apart a people from the other nations who were His, who reflected His glory, so He raised up a man, Abraham, through whom He would birth this nation.

When the Israelites gave themselves to the Lord and submitted to Him, they did have an impact on all the nations of the world, but they often turned away and began to become like the nations. Therefore, they did not fulfill the mandate He had given them. He desired a people redeemed and restored back to His original plan, but to do that, He had to prepare a platform through which that could happen. So God sent His son Jesus to renew us and quicken us into a new life, a new anointing, the power of the Holy Spirit, and the very nature of God.

Jesus then established the church and sent us out with the Great Commission. This is very important for us to capture. It is part of God's vision, His heart plan. The church is carrying everything that God started to do from the time of Abraham. All of that is in the Great Commission. We need to be peculiar people set apart for God, not consumed by worldliness. We are in the world, not of the world. We have the wisdom that comes from above, the wisdom of God, not the wisdom Adam and Eve sought. We are empowered with the Holy Spirit, with the heart of God. We can tap into His heart; He will tell us everything that is of the Father that we can implement and enforce on earth. He sends us out to every nation, to go and win the nations back to Himself. God commands us to go and disciple the nations, preparing them for His return. Then the judgment day will come.

If we understand the purpose for which God created the church, then we can come down to the situation analysis of today and say, "When God looks at the church in the nations today, what does He see? What is in His heart?"

If you look at where the church is in its mission and you see that the Day is fast approaching, along with all that comes with it, then hold up your ministry with that picture as the backdrop, it gives you a different picture of your mandate and the work that God has given you.

▶ **Exercise:**

Look at your mandate with this as a backdrop. How does this affect your view of the mission as opposed to just looking at it in a general sense? ___

___

___

How does this new view differ from your previous view? ___

___

___

When we see our mission against the backdrop of God's vision, which we can begin to grasp as we study the eras, then we can begin to identify with servants of God in the scripture, like Paul, who said, "I consider my life worth nothing to me, if only I may finish the race and complete the task the Lord Jesus has given me" (Acts 20:24).

This should create in us a sense of urgency and a deep connection with the Lord's heart. The Lord has said that the last days are fast approaching. The vessel of the church is not in the shape He wanted it to be, the nations have not been won to the Lord, and darkness is increasing. The church has lost its bearing in all of this. We have a church that wants to be like the world; it doesn't capture the heart's desire of what God began to establish with Abraham, of being a people set apart to God. This is the situation analysis of the time in we are in.

And what is in the heart of God? The urgency of saying, "I will arise. I will save my own people. I will intervene." And how will He do it? He is coming as a warrior, as a mighty God. He said, "I'll bare my right arm, and I'll fight and shake the nations." He promised that there would be shakings, there would be trials, and many other fearful things, but He is raising up an army that is going to fight.

This is not just a matter of doing good works. This is about fighting the darkness and setting captives free, and doing it with urgency because the time is so short. We are not being called to do what the apostles did 2,000 years ago; we are being called to a completely different mandate. It is a mandate of "do or die." It is urgent; it is calling for people willing not only to live for Him, but to die for Him.

This is God's vision, and we need to pray into it daily so it is written on our hearts and we know how to carry it. As we look at the times in which we live from the perspective of God's heart, and we pray into that daily, we begin to carry the mission with a greater intensity, urgency, and depth than we ever will without that backdrop or understanding.

In the New Testament, the apostles had all the reasons to quit many, many times. Paul reached a point where he said, "Woe unto me if I do not preach." It's like, "If I had my way out, I would quit, but what would then be the purpose of my life?" "Woe unto me if I don't preach." And he came to a place where he said, "For me to die is gain. For me to live is Christ." When you listen to the words Paul says, they are coming from a person who has continuously sought the heart of God for his life. That is why he says,

- "I consider my life worth nothing" (Acts 20:24)
- "I have fought the good fight, I have finished the race, I have kept the faith" (2 Timothy 4:7)
- "I consider everything a loss compared to the surpassing greatness of knowing Christ Jesus my Lord" (Philippians 3:7)
- "I press on to take hold of that for which Christ Jesus took hold of me" (Philippians 3:12)

Praying Into God's Vision. God's vision has many components. Having an understanding of it is important and vital. Catching God's vision would include

- Seeing the scope of His mission throughout the ages
- Seeing the importance of fulfilling it
- Seeing when people fulfilled it and when they did not
- Seeing the fullness of the mandate that He's given to the church in our day
- Seeing the cost that God paid to make provision for His vision

- Seeing how He came to meet us, began to call us into the mandate, and prepared us so we could fulfill it
- Seeing where the church is in fulfilling that mandate
- Seeing what is coming and what's at stake if we don't fulfill the mandate
- Seeing what we need to fight to see it fulfilled
- Seeing all of this from the perspective of the sacrifice that He made, the love that He had, the urgency that He has
- Seeing that there is a Day approaching, along with the things that He said would be coming with that (the darkness, deception, love growing cold, etc)

If we see all this and begin to pray into it, we will begin to carry it in a greater depth in our hearts.

The more we pray into God's vision, the more clearly we will begin to see it. The more we begin to see it, the more it will be impressed deeply upon our hearts. We must seek the Lord daily, praying into every component of the mandate (declaring, proclaiming, and trusting each component). When we pray into all the components of the mandate, our faith will rise, our vision will be expanded, we will begin to stand in position more firmly, and we will begin to have insight into God's vision, the bigger picture of His mission, and it will be what burns in our heart.

If we give ourselves fully to pray into these things, we would begin to capture a greater sense of God's heart and of what He's called us to do. Then we'll be able to pray from the deepest place in our heart, as Paul did, "*I must* take hold of Him for the reason that He's taken hold of me" (Philippians 3:12).

Time for Reflection:

What is the most meaningful statement or scripture you read today? ______________________________

What does God want you to do in response to this? ______________________________

As you pray your prayer target for this day/week, what are you feeling the Holy Spirit is saying or calling you to and what is the warfare coming against you? ______________________________

▶ **Prayer Time:**

Pray for God's grace to catch the vision of His heart. Go deeper into His Spirit and cry out that He would reveal His ideal desires for us today, His mission for how to accomplish those desires, and your role in that work.

Lesson 3.

God's Mandate to Man: Covenantal Position

Covenantal position is a spiritual place or position of my will, my heart, and my life being yielded to God; I trust Him and believe Him to be who He says He is. This is a real position where my life is released to Him and I am trusting Him and believing Him in every sense of the word. I am therefore free to follow, hear, obey, receive, and be led—I am free for Him to flow His life through me to do His work.

You can fail in many things, but if you move out of your covenantal position, you will find it increasingly difficult to fulfill the mandate God gives you. You will find it impossible to be able to do the work that He's commissioned you to do, and you will find yourself losing sight of Him, unsure of how to go forward, unable to draw upon His power, and know His heart.

Testimony

Staying in covenantal position is remaining in the position of total trust and surrender, abiding in His presence, and obeying His instructions.

To maintain my position, I have to daily keep myself in communion and fellowship with Him, allowing the Holy Spirit to lead me and His word to be the yardstick that I need to follow; this enables me to stay focused on the Lord.

—Joyce Nantongo
WTM International Coordinator of Prayer and Missionary to the Nations

Covenantal position is the key to walking in our mandate.

God's Mandate — Component 3: Covenantal Position

Covenantal position is a place of total surrender and trust before God, a place where we are given over to Him and trusting Him to faithfully be God in our lives. Covenantal position is staying in that place of communion, abiding, and dependency where we are trusting God with our whole heart and life. This is the place where He begins to unfold His plans to us, where He can begin to reveal to us the things that He calls us to do, and where we can begin to trust His power.

That is the covenant in which we can trust:

- He is our God; we are His people.
- We were bought with a price; our lives are no longer our own.

There will be different implications for different people, and God will also continue to deepen covenantal position as we mature, follow Him, and become more and more fully under His mandate.

Paul is a good example of standing firmly in covenantal position. The Lord appeared to Paul on the road to Damascus and told him that he would be a witness and minister to His people (Acts 9:15, 26:16). God would protect him and send him to the people to open their eyes and bring them from darkness to light (Acts 26:17-18). All he needed to ask in every situation was "How am I to be a witness here?" If it meant dying, then Paul said, "Let that be the way I witness" (Philippians 1:20-21). He knew that if he turned away from submission to Christ in any way, covenant would be broken and he would no longer be the witness God called him to be. His life was fully yielded to the Lord.

When you understand covenant and covenantal position, you will be compelled to do things even when you are fearful. People constantly warned Paul about what was coming; they even warned him not to go to Jerusalem, but Paul tells them, "Why are you weeping and breaking my heart? I am ready not only to be bound, but also to die in Jerusalem for the name of the Lord Jesus" (Acts 21:13). Paul was convinced that the One who called him said He was going to protect him; the One to whom he had given his life was responsible for his well-being. For Paul, "to live is Christ and to die is gain" (Philippians 1:21). He wanted to lay hold of that for which Christ had laid hold of him (Philippians 3:12). Everything else was not his concern, but the concern of the One who had called him and taken his life in His hands.

God called Paul to be a witness and a minister of the gospel, and that is all he determined to be, whether he was deserted, imprisoned, beaten, or perplexed. He knew who he was in Christ (2 Corinthians 4). This man, when he was about to die, said that he had finished the race and fought the good fight, keeping the faith (2 Timothy 4:7). That meant that day by

Testimony

As I go out to do the work God has called me to do, I find that it is absolutely vital to stay in covenantal position. Fulfilling the Lord's mandate is so beyond human ability and draws such warfare that without being in that place of trust and abandonment in Him, the enemy is able to hit me in ways that can attack my confidence, my faith, and my spiritual strength.

When standing in covenantal position, I can stand against the warfare, I can see the way forward to do God's work, and I can carry the purposes that He's given me. But if I get dislodged from this position, the warfare begins to bring anxiety and fear, I begin to find myself blind and unable to see how to fulfill His work, and I find my heart shrinking back from the challenges before me.

I have found that it is dangerous to go long without standing in a place that my life is completely trusting and yielded to His will and His ways, so I have made it a priority in my life to daily seek to be strengthened, focused, and going deeper in my abandonment and trust in God. This is something that I pray into every single day.

–Pastor Mark Daniel

day, he overcame the lies of the enemy that told him he was not who he thought he was, not doing the things he should be doing. Paul overcame and thought like a new creature, not like an old one. He did not fight in the old mindset, but from the place of trust and surrender and faith.

Do you see Paul's surrender and trust? Do you see his dependency on God? Paul came to such a place of abandonment to fulfill the purposes of God that He said, "I consider my life worth nothing to me, if only I may finish the race and complete the task the Lord Jesus has given me" (Acts 20:24).

Testimony

For me, covenantal position is like someone who is in love. My heart belongs to the Lord and His desires are my desires. There is deep security and rest in my soul because I know who He is and what He will do. I do not have to fret or fear and I do not have to make things happen. All the power, authority, grace, gentleness, insight, wisdom, etc, come from this place. When I am in covenantal position, there is nothing that I am afraid that I am going to "miss" or "mess up"; I can just be.

I seek to go deeper every day. I have found that if I am not going deeper with the Lord, then I am actually slipping backward. I must live a lifestyle of praise and worship, and I must be in His word every day. I have found that I must obey everything that He is saying; He really does not accept compromise. As I do these things, God leads me deeper into prayer, which makes me more in love with Him and takes me deeper into His purposes, even if I can't see it at the time.

—Kelly Sorensen

▸ **Exercise:**

Meditate on all the challenges that Paul faced and the choices that he made about how he was going to deal with them. Think about how he fought so often to stay in that yielded position, no matter what circumstance he was facing.

In your own words, describe what choices Paul made that helped him stand firmly in his covenantal position with the Lord, whether he was in jail or being beaten. ________

____

____

____

____

What choices do you need to make in your life so you can stand more firmly in a place of surrender and trust before God? ________________

____

____

____

____

Paul's dependency and trust in God helped him stay in covenantal position with the Lord; it was this position that enabled Paul to bear much fruit in his life.

Covenantal position is not a place of doing; it is a place of being: being absolutely yielded and believing and trusting God.

Fighting for Covenantal Position

The enemy seeks to come against our faith, our trust, and our surrender to God. He seeks to cause us to pull back our hearts and withdraw some levels of our trust and faith. This is a daily strategy that he uses against every believer; he will use our wounds, exaggerated thoughts, and circumstances to try to get us to lay down our covenantal position.

Covenantal position is something that we must fight for; we must continually give ourselves to uphold and strengthen it. It is a direct link between us and God, and we must continually deepen that communion.

▸ **Exercise:**

Review the testimonies in this lesson and the examples of Paul's life. What do you see are keys to fight against the attacks that will come against your abandonment to God? ____________________

____

____

____

____

____

____

____

____

Testimony

Staying in covenant position keeps me in the presence of God and keeps the environment open for Him to work. It is an active place, a place of constant surrender, yielding to Christ's nature and will over my nature and will; a place that requires a continual fight for trust and abandonment, and yet a place of rest, trust, and peace; a place of intimacy, abiding, and sweet fellowship.

To stay in covenant position I can make nothing about myself, but must be about the Lord's purposes alone, keeping my eyes on Him and continually turning into Him in humility, dependency, and nothingness to allow Him to be everything.

It is a daily battle and walk to stay in covenant position because so much comes to try to knock us out of position. Saturating in the word each day and fellowshipping with others around the word is part of the foundation for me to stay in position, as is spending prolonged times each day drawing into the presence of God, praying and seeking His heart, surrendering and encountering Him. Without daily seeking to go deeper and pressing into the Lord, I know that my life would begin to drift off course.

—Clare Hamilton

Time for Reflection:

What is the most meaningful statement or scripture you read today? ______________________________

What does God want you to do in response to this? ______________________________

As you pray your prayer target for this day/week, what are you feeling the Holy Spirit is saying or calling you to and what is the warfare coming against you? ______________________________

▸ **Prayer Time:**

Pray into your covenantal position. Seek the Lord to show you all aspects of it, spend time praising Him for choosing you as a vessel through which He will do His work, then ask Him to reveal how you can walk in the fullness of this position.

Lesson 4.

God's Mandate to Man Continued

Standing in the position of our mandate is how God fulfills the work through us. We have begun to see the importance of holding onto our commission, catching the vision of God's heart, and fighting for our covenantal position; we are now going to look at how God's commandments and instructions protect us and keep us safe.

God's Mandate — Component 4: Commandments & Instructions

When God gives a mandate to man, it includes commandments and instructions. You can study every Bible character and see that God gave each of them specific things to do or not to do. He said to them, "This is your mission that I'm sending you to accomplish, and here are the ways I want you to carry it out. To fulfill that commission, here are the things you're supposed to do." In other words, God gives instructions. Although they sometimes may seem limiting, these are what keep us in our right position to do the work.

▸ **Exercise:**

Read Joshua 1:1-9. List places in these scriptures that speak about Joshua's...

1. Vision of God's heart: ____________________
____
2. Commissioning: ____________________
____
3. Covenantal position: ____________________
____
4. Commandments and instructions: ____________________
____
5. Gifts and promises: ____________________
____
6. Grace and anointing to do the work: ____________________
____

These scriptures clearly depict the mandate God gave Joshua, revealing the vision of God's heart as well as Joshua's commissioning, the territory in which he was to operate, and what he would establish in the

Testimony: World Trumpet Mission

Many years ago, the Lord gave World Trumpet Mission our commissioning. He said, "I want you to go to the nations. I want you to blow the trumpet. I want you to warn My people. I want you to tell them the season of time called the Day of the Lord is coming soon. The Day will catch them not ready and unprepared, and they will not survive."

We rejoiced in our hearts that God had called us. But after a few days, we thought, "What is new that we are going to take to the world? People have said these kinds of things for ages. We don't know how to do this work. Going out and saying, "'Hey, Jesus is coming soon. Repent!' What is new about that?" Then we realized that we didn't know how to do this work and decided to humble ourselves and fast, asking the Lord to show us how to do the work.

Personally, my idea was to ask Him to give us signs and wonders that would be so overwhelming people would know that surely the Lord had sent us. But when we went before the Lord, He said to us, "By yourselves, you cannot do My work. It's only I who can work through you. The most important thing you need is to position yourselves in such a way that I can work through you. This is how you are to do it: first, give Me your lives completely. Let it sink into your hearts, beyond a doubt, that your lives are no longer your own. They are Mine. You have no right on your life. You have no permission to use your life the way you want. You have no say on your life. It's mine. I'll tell you what to do. I'll use it the way I want. I'll take it into the circumstances I want, and I'll demand on your lives what I want. If you humble yourselves and adopt that attitude, then I'll work through you.

The second thing you need to know is that from now on, there is no reason for you to be alive except to do what I've called you to do. It's the only purpose for your life. In other words, if you cannot fulfill your purpose, you would rather die. It's the only reason you are on earth, so whatever you do, whatever you plan, whatever you think, whatever you involve yourself in, it must have one purpose: to fulfill what I've called you to do and to do a good work.

The third thing is to adopt unconditional love. Don't relate to people because they are easy to get along with. Relate with people because I love them and died for them. Don't judge them, don't undermine anyone, don't pay back evil for evil. Submit yourselves to love.

If you take those three foundational stones and make them the pillars of your life, I will work through you. Your lives will be like an open channel for Me."

Brethren, that's what we mean when we talk about covenantal positioning. God was saying to us, "If you will do this, then I will fulfill what I promised you." That is what we are to stand and fight for, and a lot of surrender and trust is needed to stay in that.

The instructions the Lord gave were very clear. Many times, whenever someone on our team began to take offense, hold onto a hurt, or make a situation about themselves, they would repent because they remembered that God had told us we could not have such behavior. We followed the instructions God gave us, and that kept us in that place of surrender and being before God.

God gave us these three foundational things; that was our point of surrender and trust, our covenantal position, and we had to fight to stay in that place. God also gave us instructions and requirements to enable us to stay in such a yielded place. As He directed us, we began to saturate in His word and live a lifestyle of worship and praise. He showed us we could not allow negativity in our hearts. We had to persevere and prevail in prayer, push through the darkness, and not settle for not breaking through. He required us to subdue the flesh, along with many other things. If we did not follow these instructions, our surrender would begin to weaken, our faith would come under attack, and we would begin to allow distrust, negativity, doubt, fear, and all kinds of things to come into our lives and steal our place of dependency and trust in the Lord.

Sometimes we felt like the instructions were too hard or too limiting. "It's too much. I don't feel the strength to be in the word of God, to read a lot of the word. I don't feel the spirit to praise the Lord, to exalt Him, to pray, to wage warfare. I don't feel the strength to wait upon Him." But brothers and sisters, those instructions were for our own good. They are what kept—and still keep—us in the position that is required for God to work through us.

Promised Land. God also gave Joshua promises, instructions, and grace and anointing to do the work. He promised to give Joshua every place where he set his foot, that He would be with Joshua as He was with Moses, that He would never leave or forsake Joshua, and that He would be with Joshua wherever he went. God was promising to take care of Joshua in every circumstance, and, more importantly, He was fulfilling the promise He had made to Abraham: "You will lead these people to inherit the land I swore to their forefathers to give them" (Joshua 1:6). God wanted to fulfill the vision and desires of His heart through Joshua.

God also gave Joshua commandments and instructions:

- Be strong and courageous
- Be careful to obey My law
- Meditate on My word day and night
- Do not be afraid
- Do not be discouraged

Joshua was coming into the position where He could do the work God gave him, and these instructions kept him from turning away from the purposes of God. He was told, "You must be in the place of absolute trust and surrender to me. You cannot doubt even for a second." If Joshua had not followed the instructions and commands of the Lord, he would have failed to fulfill the commission God had given him of leading the children of Israel into the Promised Land.

Following the Commandments and Instructions God Gives Us

Samson did not take his instructions seriously (Judges 13-16); he treated them casually instead of holy and precious. He did not realize that the implications of ignoring the instructions and commandments from God would be far bigger and more damaging than he could imagine. Samson was called to deliver Israel from the Philistines (Judges 13:5), but instead ended up being their captive. He lost his power and strength as a consequence of breaking the instructions God had given him (Judges 16:18-20). The Philistines gouged out his eyes. He became a slave and a laughing stock, a toy the Philistines would bring out and make fun of (Judges 16:21,25). Samson was taken out of his destiny because he failed to follow the instructions the Lord gave him.

We can see similar stories today. Sadly, we have seen pastors fall because of their immorality, greed, etc. They cannot fulfill their destiny because they have failed to treasure and follow the commandments and instructions of the Lord.

We are all weak; we all fail. Tell your soul, "Obey the Lord, O my soul," because you don't even know the meaning or importance of the instructions the Lord has given you.

▶ **Exercise:**

Read Psalm 119:33-72. List five things David requested of the Lord in these verses.

1. ______________________________
2. ______________________________
3. ______________________________
4. ______________________________
5. ______________________________

List some key words David uses to describe the instructions of the Lord:

____

____

What strikes you about David's attitude toward the instructions of God?

____

____

____

Throughout all of Psalm 119, David keeps crying out, "Lord, teach me Your instructions; teach me Your statutes. Help me to hide Your word in my heart. Keep my feet following Your ways." David had learned that the instructions of the Lord are precious—that they are life itself—and he continued to pray himself into submission and abandonment to those instructions. This is a discipline that we find ourselves needing; we must pray ourselves into this mandate on a daily basis.

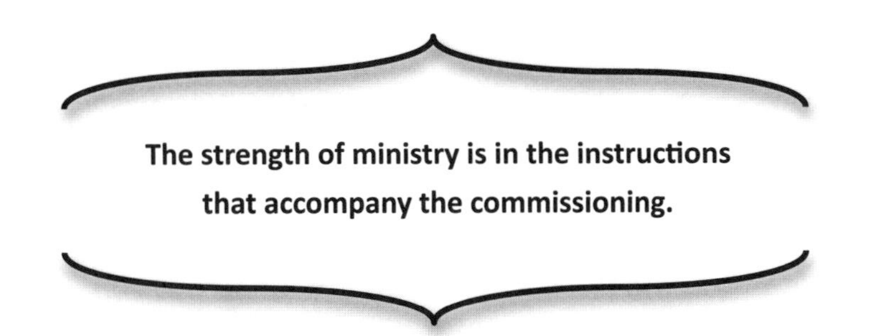

What keeps us in covenant position, where God can work powerfully through us and fulfill His commission, is in the instructions He gives us. You can look throughout the Bible and find that every person God called was given instructions. King Solomon is a good example. His father David told him, "If you follow the instructions God has given, He will fulfill destiny through you. He will rule this land through you. But if you do not follow these commands, you will lose the position that He has given you." Solomon gradually began to walk away from the instructions of God: he married foreign women, allowed idolatry into the land, and turned away from the ways of the Lord. Instead of following God's instructions, Solomon began to do what seemed right to him, and he lost everything.

The instructions keep us fully in position, which enable God to fulfill His commissioning through us.

▸ **Exercise:**

What are some of the instructions and commands that God has given you? ____________________

____

____

God's Mandate — Component 5: Gifts and Promises

The mandate that God gives man also includes gifts and promises. God gives gifts and promises to every person that He calls into ministry. He says, "I'll do this with you." He promised Joshua that He would be with Joshua just as He was with Moses.

▸ **Exercise:**

Read the following verses. What promises did God give to each of these men?

Joshua 1:3-5: ____________________

____

____

Jeremiah 1:18: ____________________

____

____

1 Kings 2:4: ____
____
____

Luke 4:18: ____
____
____

The Promises of God to Joshua

- I will give you every place where you set your foot
- Your territory will extend from the desert to Lebanon, and from the Euphrates to the Great Sea
- No one will be able to stand up against you all the days of your life
- As I was with Moses, so I will be with you
- I will never leave you nor forsake you
- You will lead these people to inherit the land I swore to their forefather to give them
- You will be successful wherever you go
- You will be prosperous and successful
- The Lord your God will be with you wherever you go.

Joshua 1:3-9

God promised Joshua that no one would be able to stand against him all the days of his life and that He would always be with him as He was with Moses. God promised to help make Jeremiah strong—an iron pillar and a bronze wall. He said that no one would be able to overcome Jeremiah, and promised that He would be with him and rescue him. God made a covenant with David and promised that the house of David would always have someone on the throne of Israel; David declares that promise over his son Solomon. Jesus said that He had been anointed by God to open the eyes of the blind and to set the captives free.

God has given us promises as well: His indwelling presence, that He would always be with us, that He would never leave us or forsake us, that He has given us all authority, and so much more. He promised to guide, to lead, to teach; to give us His wisdom and show us the way. He said He would go before us and be with us wherever we go. As we are living a life that is abandoned to Him, He also begins to speak personal promises over us, revealing to us the things that He is going to do through us, just as He did with the people in the Bible. We are to believe all these promises, to hold them up in the midst of battle.

Think about the promise that God gave Joshua: "I will be with you as I was with Moses." Joshua had seen the presence of God come and sit with Moses; he saw God shake the nations, swallow up Korah and his rebellion, provide water from a rock, defeat Israel's enemies, and provide food and water in the wilderness.

How many times did Joshua have to hold up the promise that God was with him as He had been with Moses? As the Israelites went into battle after battle, how many times did Joshua hold up this promise? As he heard about the forces that are advancing against them, as the fears were trying to crush in around him, how many times did he pray into that promise that "God is with us as He was with Moses"? That is what gave Joshua the strength and the courage to stand, to rise up and fulfill the mandate that God had given him.

Testimony: Hudson Taylor

"He must move men through God — by prayer," that was the philosophy of J. Hudson Taylor, first missionary to the interior of China and the founder of the China Inland Mission. And from that December day when as a teenager he heard from Heaven, "Go for Me to China, "this young Englishman set out to prove his philosophy. That he did so successfully and miraculously makes for some of the most exciting reading in the records of evangelism.

After his call Taylor first moved from the comforts of his home with his parents and two sisters in beautiful Barnsley of Yorkshire to Drainside, Hull, a poverty-stricken, depressing area named after and notorized by its foul ditch. Taylor had gone there purposely to work for a doctor and accumulate a little medical knowledge, and also to accustom himself to something of the loneliness and dangers of living in a strange land where his only companion would be God.

It was at Drainside Taylor learned one can trust God with his last cent. He had been called out late one night to witness to and pray over a sick woman with starving children. As he tried to pray, his words choked in his mouth because he had in his possession a silver coin that would answer his prayer and alleviate their sufferings somewhat. "Hypocrite!" he heard his heart condemn him. "Telling people about a kind and loving Father in Heaven — *and not prepared to trust Him yourself,* without your money!" He gave them his last coin—only one bowl of porridge between him and poverty! As he ate that last meal he remembered the Scripture, "He that giveth to the poor lendeth to the Lord."

The next day he received a package. In it was a gold coin — worth ten times the silver coin. Taylor cried out triumphantly, "That's good interest! Ha! Ha! Invested in God's bank for twelve hours and it brings me this! That's the bank for me!" Thus at nineteen years of age, Taylor learned he could trust and obey God in every area of his life.

Praying! And answers to prayer! That became the passion of his life. He learned to move men through God by prayer. He asked no man for any material thing. He laid all needs before his Lord. That doctor he had worked for at Drainside had suggested to his young assistant, "Taylor, please do remind me when it is time to pay your salary. I'm so busy, you know, I'm quite likely to forget." And forget he did. But Taylor remembered that in China he would have no one to ask anything of, only God, so he simply asked God to remind the doctor.

Three weeks later the doctor remembered — but only after he had banked his money. Taylor was broke. It was Saturday. He had no money to pay his rent. He had no money for food. He prayed as he worked until ten o'clock, glad he would not have to face his landlady. As he prepared to leave, the doctor surprised him, "What do you think? One of my patients has just come to pay his bill! He's one of my richest patients and he could have paid me by check anytime. Yet, there he is, bringing in the money at ten o'clock on Saturday night." Then he added, "By the way, Taylor, you might as well take these notes. I have no change, but I can give you the balance of your salary next week ... Good night!"

Taylor's prayers were answered. He could not only pay his rent, he had money in hand for weeks ahead — but more than that, he had proven again: *God answers prayer and moves men.* He could go on to China!

(Reprinted with permission from *Profiles in Evangelism* by Fred Barlow, Sword of the Lord Publishers, ©1976.)

▶ **Exercise:**

God gives us a mission and the only way to fulfill it is to hold the spiritual position of the mandate. Write out the six components of mandate:

1. ________________________________
2. ________________________________
3. ________________________________
4. ________________________________
5. ________________________________
6. ________________________________

The promises are precious. God gives us a mission that the only way possible for us to fulfill is to stand in all of our mandate. As we give our heart to fulfilling God's vision, to accepting and choosing to stay on the course of our commissioning, as we fight to stay in that place of surrender and trust, as we begin to submit our lives to His instructions and commands, and as we also hold onto and believe in the gifts and promises that He's given us, they encourage, uplift, and strengthen us in the walk and in the battles, and they give us the resolve to persevere to see God's heart desires fulfilled.

We cannot hold onto just one or two components of the mandate; we need to be praying into every one of them. There are so many things that come against us that try to get us to lose heart, to minimize the mission of God, to settle for just doing tasks and not seeing the fulfillment of what God has spoken. Joshua had to keep holding up the promises that God had given him, and at the end of his life he was able to say to the Israelites, "not one of all the good promises the Lord your God gave you has failed. Every promise has been fulfilled; not one has failed" (Joshua 23:14).

We are not only praying to stay in surrender and trust, to live a lifestyle that is following the instructions that God has given us, but we are also holding onto God's promises, proclaiming and declaring them.

▸ **Exercise:**

What are some of the promises that God has spoken into your life? ____

____

____

God's Mandate — Component 6: Grace & Anointing to Do the Work

The mandate that God gives man also includes the grace and anointing to do the work. He gives everyone He's called the grace to do the work. Without that grace and anointing, we can do nothing.

Paul tells us that "God is able to make all grace abound to you, so that in all things at all times, having all that you need, you will abound in every good work" (2 Corinthians 9:8). God is the only one who can open every door; He is the only one who can bring the pieces together or to give the strength to do the work He has called us to do. Without His grace, we will never see His work fulfilled. When we are faced with the impossible or insurmountable, the places where we don't know how to get through, we have to believe that His grace is sufficient to do what we cannot do ourselves. We constantly rely on His grace, His unmerited favor, to do what we cannot do in ourselves, to bring together what we cannot bring together, to show the way when there doesn't seem to be a way, that His grace is sufficient to carry this work through to completion.

Bringing It All Together—Praying Into the Mandate

We declare our mandate into the heavenlies. We declare it unto our own soul. We declare it unto everything that sets itself up against fulfilling the purposes to which He's called us to. We begin to rise up into position and to go forward as a member of God's army to begin

Praying Into the Mandate

- First, we begin to pray into His commissioning and to treat as holy the calling that He's put upon our lives. We begin to hold up and declare that we have been set apart for His purposes, that we belong to Him, and that He has called us into this time and this day. We being to lay out our position of trust, and abandon ourselves into that place of trusting Him and yielding our lives, declaring that "My life is not mine; it belongs to Him." And that in spite of everything that makes our hearts want to shrink back or cover over, we choose to abandon ourselves and trust Him fully.
- We then pray into understanding the burden of God's heart, the seriousness and depth of what He has been doing throughout the centuries, what He's brought us to at this time, and the season of time we are going into in the nations and the church, and we begin to carry the burden that God has.
- We begin to submit and yield ourselves to the instructions and commands He's given us as He's molding us and shaping us to be vessels that He can use. We begin to hold those up and bow our knees in obedience.
- We hold onto God's promises so that as the enemy comes against us and tries to intimidate us, to get us to shrink back, we are holding the promises up as a banner, declaring what we have been called to do.
- As we face mountains that are too big and challenges that are beyond us, we don't become timid or cower, but we hold up the grace that He has given us: "My God's grace is sufficient to see everything through. He cannot fail. He will be faithful to complete this work."

to see His purposes advancing. We pray ourselves into our mandate day by day by day. We trust that each part of His mandate is essential, and we fight to grab hold of the truth of each one. We believe that our God is faithful and that He will bring us into the position we need to be standing in to do the work that He is requiring of us.

> We may all pray differently and every day will look a little different, but this is still something that is deepening and growing and becoming a part of us.

Praying into God's mandate is essential to our lives. It is a daily discipline that is necessary to be an active and fruitful member of God's army.

Time for Reflection:

What is the most meaningful statement or scripture you read today? ______________________

What does God want you to do in response to this? ______________________

As you pray your prayer target for this day/week, what are you feeling the Holy Spirit is saying or calling you to and what is the warfare coming against you? ______________________

▸ **Prayer Time:**

Using the chart on the previous page ("Praying Into the Mandate"), spend time praying into the fullness of your mandate.

Week 6.

Creating the Atmosphere That God Requires

GOAL OF THE WEEK:

In the following lessons, we will discuss the importance of creating an atmosphere in which God can work. We will discover that to fulfill the purposes of God—to even recognize and understand what His mission, goals, and objectives are—we need to create an atmosphere that will draw the presence of God.

The matters we are dealing with are big. We have seen the state of the nations and the state of the church, and our hearts are stirred. We want to see the church awakened and our homes, churches, cities, and nations transformed. We dream of the church rising up in power, of being relevant in these last days, of opening up the spiritual atmosphere over our cities, of giving hope to the nations, and of seeing God's kingdom being established. This is not a small thing that God has laid on our hearts.

If we look at ourselves, we may lose faith. Can we accomplish such a big vision? We tend to shrink back from things that appear to be too big or too difficult, but remember the apostles of Jesus Christ. All of them ran away while He was being arrested, all but one of them abandoned Him at the cross, and even after they found the empty tomb, not one of them believed that He had risen. Yet, it was to them that He said, "Go and make disciples of all nations" (Matthew 28:19). They may not have looked like the kind of troop that could accomplish such a great thing, but we know from history that they did.

Jesus came to these men who had failed, abandoned, and denied Him, and He promised them, "You will be my witnesses in Jerusalem, and in all Judea and Samaria, and to the ends of the earth" (Acts 1:8). But He also said to them, "Stay in the city until you have been clothed with power from on high" (Luke 24:49). Jesus was giving them their

Prayer targets for week 6:

1. Draw deeper into the Spirit of God. Allow Him to reveal to you what hinders you from drawing near to Him as well as what strengthens your ability to draw near to Him. He has promised that as we draw near to Him, He will draw near to us.

2. Begin to spend longer times in prayer. Press into the Lord deeper. Seek to draw further into His presence. This is a key to our understanding of creating an atmosphere that draws the presence of the Holy Spirit.

commission to "Go and do" as well as instructions to wait till they had received the power of the Holy Spirit. He promised them that when the Holy Spirit came, they would be clothed with power and would be His witnesses throughout the earth. And He fulfilled that promise.

In our studies over the past few weeks, we identified key principles we need to understand to do the works that God requires:

1. Ministry is not doing good activities; it is fulfilling what the heart of God desires to be accomplished.
2. As we analyzed the eras we began to see His heart and mission.

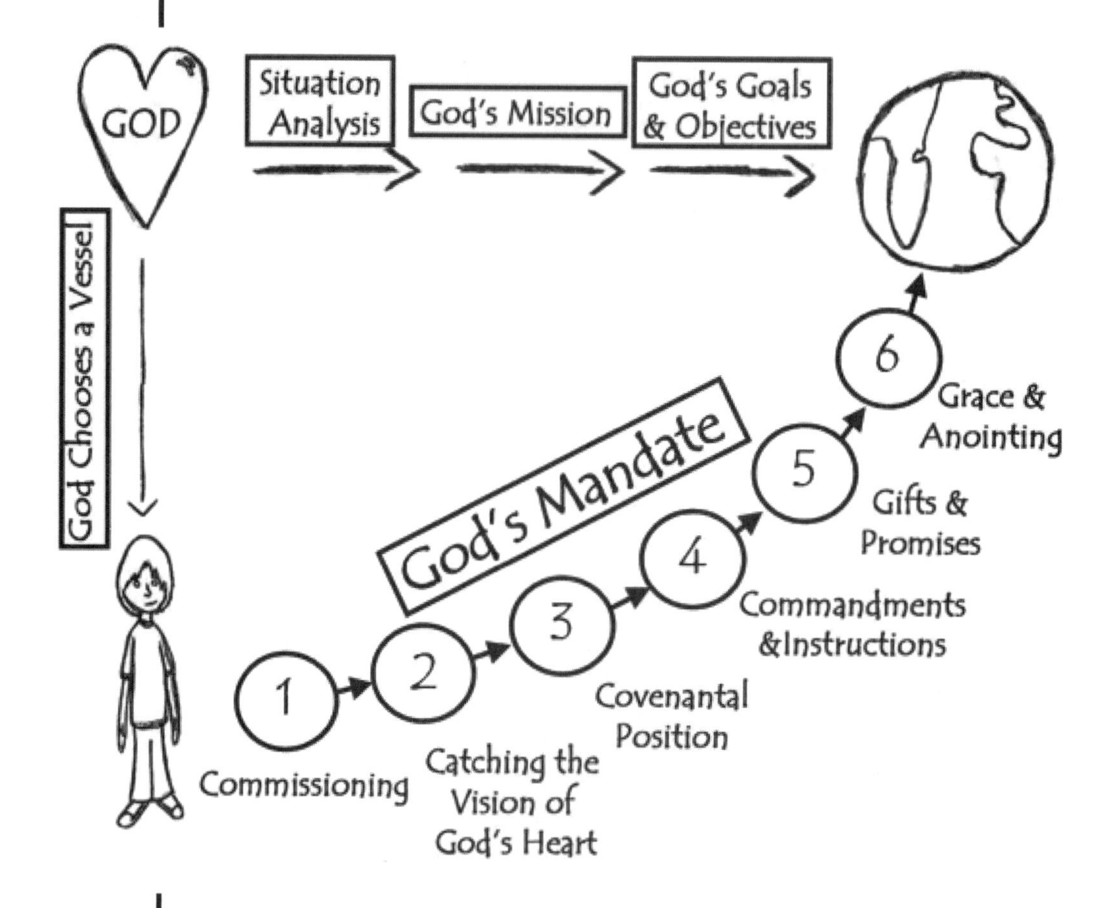

God is always at work. He analyzes the situation, then sets a mission for Himself. The mission includes goals and objectives of what God desires to see take place. He then calls a man or woman to be part of that work and gives them a mandate. The mandate includes envisioning, commissioning, covenantal position, instructions and requirements, gifts and promises, and the grace and anointing to do the work.

It is our mandate that helps us remain focused on the work of God. It provides security, direction, power, and authority. It is also a source of strength in times of battle and of faith that our God can and will do things through us that we cannot do ourselves. It is by standing in the fullness of our mandate, like the disciples, that we will be empowered and enabled to turn our own world upside down.

The issue we are then faced with is,

- "How do we know what God's mission is?"
- "How do we clearly understand what He is calling us to do?"
- "How do we successfully work the works that God requires of us?"
- "How do we tap into the power of the Holy Spirit?"

In the following lessons, we will discuss the importance of creating an atmosphere in which God can work. We will discover that to fulfill the purposes of God—to even recognize and understand what His mission, goals, and objectives are—we need to create an atmosphere that will draw the presence of God. This is most crucial, as without God, without the presence of His Holy Spirit, we will be unable to clearly hear His voice or to understand the work we are being called into and the mandate we are being given. We would not have the power to do the work that God is calling us to do, and we would be unable to fulfill the desires of His heart.

Sadly, this also means we would be unable to push back the darkness and to see the church awakened, the lost saved, and the nations discipled—all those things that the Lord desires and that are now burning in our own hearts.

The key question now is, "How do we create the atmosphere that draws the presence of God?"

Lesson 1.
The Presence of the Holy Spirit

God has got a mission, and it is pursuing this mission that constitutes His work. The first mission God set for Himself was to reveal the mystery of who He is, to reveal His glory. His desire was to do this through creation (Romans 1:29, Psalm 19:1-4). That was His mission and He set out to do it. As He worked the work of creation, He periodically did a situation analysis and "saw that it was good" (Genesis 1:4,10,12,18,21,25,31). Everything was going according to plan; the work of creation was going according to His mission and He was pleased.

Look back to the very beginning of creation. Genesis 1:1-2 says, "In the beginning God created the heavens and the earth. Now the earth was formless and empty, darkness was over the surface of the deep, and the Spirit of God was hovering over the waters." All but one of the conditions described in verse 2 had changed by the end of the first chapter of Genesis. The earth was no longer formless, it was no longer empty, and it was no longer full of darkness. However, one condition remained: the Spirit of God was still hovering over creation.

What does this indicate to us? That before God began to put creation in place, He desired an atmosphere filled with the Holy Spirit. God will not work in just any circumstance (Exodus 33:14-16, Numbers 15:41-43, Joshua 7:10-12, Isaiah 59:1-2). If He is going to work He requires a certain atmosphere in which to unfold His purposes. And before He begins working, or unfolding and unveiling His work, He wants the environment—the atmosphere to be created—filled with the presence of the Holy Spirit (Matthew 3:16, Luke 1:35, Acts 1:4-5).

Let us ask, then, "What kind of spiritual atmosphere does God work in?"

The Power of the Holy Spirit

From the beginning to the end of the Bible, you can see that any time God wanted to do something among His people, His Spirit was present. The scriptures say that "the presence of the Lord" came down, "the Spirit of the Lord" or "the hand of the Lord" came upon them, and they were empowered to do the work the Lord gave them to do (Judges 3:9-11, Judges 6:34, 1 Samuel 16:13, 2 Chronicles 20:14, Acts 6:8, Acts 13:1-4).

▸ Exercise:

Read the following verses, then answer the questions for each:
Who is the scripture referring to? What happened to this person? What was the result?

Judges 3:10-11. Who? ________________________________
What? ________________________________
Judges 6:34-35. Who? ________________________________
What? ________________________________
Judges 11:29,32-33. Who? ________________________________
What? ________________________________
1 Kings 18:46. Who? ________________________________
What? ________________________________
2 Chronicles 20:13-19. Who? ________________________________
What? ________________________________
Ezekiel 11:4-6. Who? ________________________________
What? ________________________________
Ezekiel 33:21-33. Who? ________________________________
What? ________________________________

The Spirit of God came upon Othniel and Jephthah and led them into great victories. When Gideon blew the trumpet, the Spirit of the Lord was so strong on him that everyone who heard responded to his call to arms. The prophets were able to boldly speak out the words the Lord gave them because His Spirit came upon them. In all these instances, the power of the Lord was revealed; He brought victory and strength, He gave wisdom, correction, and direction. God showed Israel and the nations who He was and what He desired.

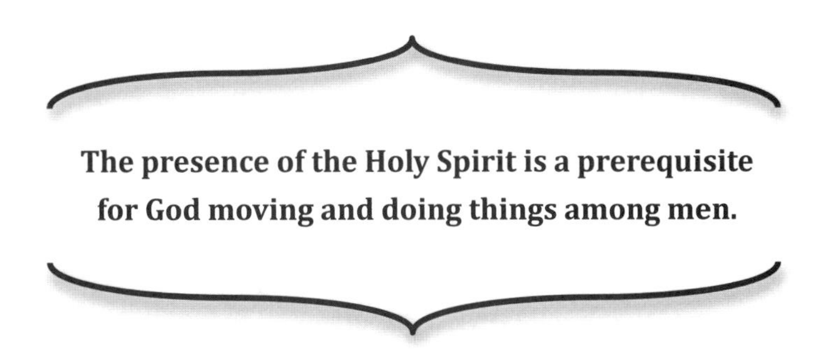

There are examples of this in the New Testament as well. On the day Jesus was baptized, the scriptures say that, "At that moment heaven was opened, and he saw the Spirit of God descending like a dove and lighting on him. And a voice from heaven said, 'This is my Son, whom I love; with him I am well pleased'" (Matthew 3:16-17). Another example is the apostles: Jesus told them to wait for the Holy Spirit (Luke 24:49); the moment He fell upon them, they were ready to begin the work (Acts 2).

The Indwelling Presence of the Holy Spirit

Genesis 2:7 says, "The Lord God formed the man from the dust of the ground and breathed into his nostrils the breath of life, and the man became a living being." This scripture illustrates another element of the atmosphere God requires: it is not enough to have the presence of the Holy Spirit around us or upon us, it is also important to have Him inside of us. This is the original design God intended: the Spirit of God filling the atmosphere and the Spirit of God inside of man.

Look at John 14:15-17: Jesus was talking to the apostles and said, "If you love me, you will obey what I command. And I will ask the Father, and he will give you another Counselor to be with you forever — the Spirit of truth. The world cannot accept him, because it neither sees him nor knows him. But you know him, for he lives with you and will be in you." Do you hear that? There is the Holy Spirit *in* you, and there is also the Holy Spirit *over* you. These are two different things.

▸ **Exercise:**

Describe the difference between the Holy Spirit within you and the Holy Spirit around you: ____

____

____

____

> The Holy Spirit is to God's kingdom what water is to fish.

An Atmosphere Full of the Holy Spirit

If God is going to work and manifest His purposes, He wants an atmosphere full of the Holy Spirit. The Holy Spirit is to God's kingdom what water is to fish. If you take fish out of water, they begin to suffocate and die. If you take the Holy Spirit out of the atmosphere, people begin to suffocate spiritually and their spiritual life soon dies.

An atmosphere full of the presence of the Holy Spirit does not mean just the presence of the Holy Spirit on one individual. It also refers to the Holy Spirit's presence over a territory or a specific location.

Remember that God has got a mission. He is at work. He has goals and objectives He wants to accomplish. But it is He who has set the environmental requirements; that is what He wants. From the beginning of Genesis, that is how He wanted things to be, and until today, He has not changed. We need to create the right atmosphere that God requires for those purposes to be fulfilled.

Testimony

In 2006, our church had begun to have a burden to see a strong move of God in our nation. We had heard Pastor John Mulinde sharing and had invited him to Orlando to lead a conference. We had made arrangements at a venue that would sit up to 600 people, and were really encouraged because George Otis let us use his mailing list to promote the meeting throughout the US.

A few weeks before the conference, only 18 people had registered! We had felt that we were going to have a serious impact in our nation through this conference, but it wasn't coming together and we were facing serious debt if it was cancelled. Although we had already been praying, we knew we needed to go deeper and started to cry out to the Lord to show us his heart.

One prayer night, about 14 of us committed to being quiet before the Lord until He spoke. After about 45 minutes, one of the ladies was compelled to read scripture (Hosea 14, NLT). The Lord said to us, "I am a jealous God." Through God's grace, he then spoke to us about the idols in our hearts, saying that He would not open the nation to us until the idols of the land were out of our own hearts.

When God showed us the idols in our hearts, we started repenting and then God began to bring the people together for this conference, which opened the doors in many cities in the US where WTM is still at work. From that time, we began to see the work going forth in the land.

One key lesson we learned was that creating the atmosphere that draws the Holy Spirit is vital and that we can't just assume we are doing that just because we are praying. We need to seek the Lord to show us either how to draw His presence or to know what is hindering the presence of the Holy Spirit from coming.

—Hunter's Creek Community Church
Orlando, FL

Three Arenas in Which to Create the Spiritual Atmosphere

The question now is, "How do we create the right atmosphere for God?" There are three arenas in which we do that:

1. Our hearts
2. The atmosphere around us
3. The system of life around us

We will be discussing these three areas in the following lessons.

Time for Reflection:

What is the most meaningful statement or scripture you read today? ______

What does God want you to do in response to this? ______

As you pray your prayer target for this day/week, what are you feeling the Holy Spirit is saying or calling you to and what is the warfare coming against you? ______

▸ Prayer Time:

Press more deeply into God's presence. Go further—and longer—before Him. Do not be afraid of hitting against "walls." Seek the Lord to go through them. We are seeking to create a deep sense of His presence.

Lesson 2.
Our Hearts: The Holy Spirit's Presence Within Us

"The Lord God formed the man from the dust of the ground and breathed into his nostrils the breath of life, and the man became a living being" (Genesis 2:7). As we saw in yesterday's lesson, this is an element of the atmosphere God requires: His presence within us. It is not enough to have the Holy Spirit's presence around us; it is important to also have Him inside of us.

For man to be able to accomplish what God created Him to do, God blew the breath of life into him. That is what connected God's heart with His Spirit, resulting in communion. This communion enables discernment of God's heart and His will, tapping into His wisdom, His knowledge, and His understanding. When people are filled with the Holy Spirit and the Spirit of God is moving upon their lives, they have understanding beyond human ability. They look at situations and see what is going on because they are tapping into God's understanding, because the Holy Spirit is the One who gives the gifts of wisdom, knowledge, revelation, and discernment. As we walk away from self-reliance and come into that deeper communion with the Holy Spirit, we see an atmosphere in which God is beginning to work.

Why is this important? Because in many cities, people come together to pray for transformation, but they don't realize that there is also work that needs to be done inside themselves. They come together and pray, "Oh God, cleanse that neighborhood of drug addicts, of prostitution, of violence." But the atmosphere outside and the reality inside, both need to have the presence and influence of the Holy Spirit.

We need to seek the Lord, "How do I allow the Holy Spirit to gain more influence over me? Over my thoughts, my feelings, my desires, my plans?" We all have times when we are overtaken by fear, discouragement, wrong desires, self-pity, all kinds of things; sometimes we accept them and they continue. We say, "I'm just going through this." But if we remembered God's plan for man to rule, we begin to realize that we are not able to see clearly, take authority over, or pray effectively unless we allow the Lord to gain the victory in our own hearts and lives.

Many times we are praying for people who we hold judgments against. We are praying for people to come through in faith, but we are still standing in doubt ourselves. We are praying for marriages, but we are still allowing lust and impurity to reside in our own hearts. We are praying for people addicted to drugs and gambling, but we are addicted to shopping and food. We are praying for people to want to come back to God, and yet He isn't our first love or deepest affection; we put things above Him. If we are serious about wanting to draw the presence of the Holy Spirit, then we must begin to deal with our own hearts, to seek God to break through these things that are in our lives, and to prepare an environment that will draw His presence.

▶ **Exercise:**

These things that can hinder us are always deeper than what we see at the surface, but there are some things that we can see. What are some things you see at the surface that you realize God needs to strip away? ______________

____

____

____

____

We must be humble here and acknowledge that we don't want to just have prayers; we truly want to draw the presence of the Holy Spirit. If we are going to pay the cost, to lay down our lives to draw the power of the Holy Spirit, we must begin to become sober, honest, and open, and allow God to begin to shine His light deeply into our own hearts.

We must be humble and acknowledge that we don't want to just have prayers; we truly want to draw the presence of the Holy Spirit.

George Otis has done research all over the world. In the videos that he produces (The Sentinel Group; www.glowtorch.org), he has documented places where the presence of God was drawn and the area began experiencing transforming revival. Interestingly, George found that it did not matter what culture, whether Indonesia or sub-Saharan Africa, an Indian tribe in North America or a city in South America, there was one common denominator in every single place: there was a group of people who began to hunger for God more than they hungered for anything else. As those people began to come together and cry out to God, allowing Him to prepare a vessel through which His presence could come and dwell, the Holy Spirit would begin to come and move in power. That is when God would begin to move in powerful ways: stadiums would fill up with people coming for prayer, God would bring unity that man couldn't create, prayer would begin to rise up, God would begin to heal the land, sectors in society would start to open; the

Holy Spirit would begin to gain control and move. But the key was always that there was a group of people who began to hunger for God and His presence more than they hungered for anything else.

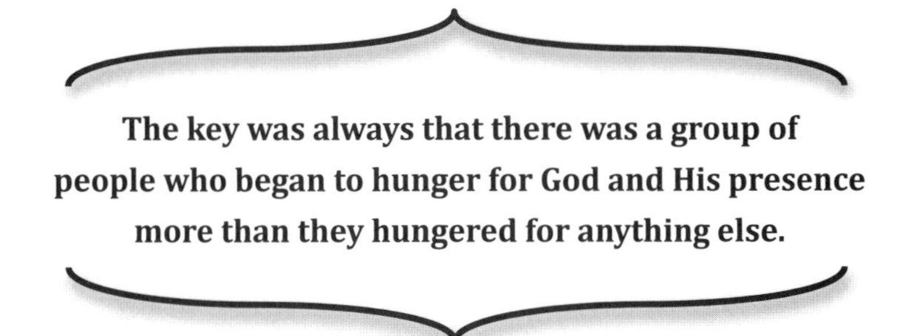

The key was always that there was a group of people who began to hunger for God and His presence more than they hungered for anything else.

▶ **Exercise:**

Are you willing for God to bring you to that place where you hunger for Him more than anything else? Please explain your answer. ______________

____

____

We need to begin to cry out for God to prepare vessels through which He can work; vessels that can pray and draw His presence. We don't want any compromises; we don't want any rationalizations or justifications. We want Him to cleanse and do whatever needs to be done so that His presence can come in might and power. It is not that we are perfected yet, but we have come to a place where our lives are abandoned to Him, we are seeking Him above everything, and we want Him to move more than we want anything else. Out of that place of desperation and surrender, we will begin to see the Holy Spirit being drawn.

The Work of the Holy Spirit in Our Hearts

There is a common way we think of preparing our hearts: through repentance, cleansing, and purifying ourselves. This is very crucial, but if it is what God is waiting for before He can come and take abode in our lives, it will never happen. We will never be perfected because we are always in the process of being perfected. Perfection only comes when we pass on into the next life.

Should we ignore repentance, then? No! It is part of the process; it is part of making our hearts ready. However, we must not allow ourselves to get caught in the trap of thinking that we must complete the act of repentance and cleansing before God will abide with us; that we must purify ourselves until there is nothing left, and that then God will take abode in our heart. That perfection will never come because, as stated above, we are always in the process of being cleansed and purified.

So what is it that God requires? Simply trust and surrender to Him, to stand in our covenantal position. A simple example is the gospel. When we preach the gospel we don't ask people to purify themselves of everything so that Christ may enter their hearts. We don't tell them that He won't enter until their hearts are completely purified. What do we ask them to do? To believe on Jesus Christ, to put their trust in Him, to give Him their lives and let Him be Lord. When that happens, He takes abode in their hearts.

They are not perfect, but when they come into that position, it is covenantal. It is the new covenant, what makes us children of God. Believing in Christ is what makes us acceptable to God, and as long as we stay in that place, God will continue His work within us. He will continue purifying us, maturing us, teaching us, and making us able to fulfill His purposes.

How do we create the right spiritual atmosphere in the heart? Through our covenantal position with Him. Yes, we need to purify ourselves, but before perfection will come our way we need to know the covenantal relationship that God has called us to. Standing in that relationship with God is what creates an abode for Him in our hearts. When you discern the instructions and requirements the Lord has given you and you obey and stand firm, when you are standing in that place of total surrender and trust in the Lord—even when you feel everything in you is resisting—you will be in the position that makes it possible for Him to come and take abode in your heart.

You may be thinking, "I don't know my covenantal position. What is it?" The simplest way to know is to go back to the day you got saved and remember the covenant you made with Jesus: to give Him your life in exchange for His life and to trust Him to take care of you into eternity. When a new convert takes the position of saying, "I put my faith in Jesus Christ. I receive Him in my heart," it is that positioning which brings Christ into His heart. That is the position from which we all started.

▸ Pause to Pray Into Position

The Bible says that when the Holy Spirit comes, he will remind you of all things. Ask the Holy Spirit to remind you of the things the Lord has spoken to you. God says different things to different people, and it is important that you remember what He has spoken to you. Some things will have to do with God revealing His heart's desires to you; others will be about your commissioning, covenantal position, the instructions or requirements He has asked you to follow, or the gifts and promises that He has given you. Cry out to the Lord to speak to you, journal anything that He tells you, then ask the Holy Spirit to teach you how to pray these things into reality in your life. ______________________________

____

____

____

____

____

Going Deeper With the Lord

To continue a deepening walk and trust in the Lord, we need to be aware of how He works. Our understanding of this will keep our focus on Him, and will help us mature in our walk, protect us from the battles that will come against us, and keep our hearts open to the work of the Holy Spirit.

When God first calls someone, He will give promises and instructions. He will give details about your commissioning as well as promises of what He is going to do in and through you. As He gives you these things, He will begin to work through you to accomplish His work; you will feel so happy and fulfilled. Then one day He will say, "I want you to move to a new level." When He says that, please be aware that the season to change is not long; there will come a time when the position you are at will become invalid.

If you choose to stay at the former level, you will realize that you can no longer go forward. You will realize that God was blessing and pouring out, His Spirit was moving, but then He said, "Go to this next step," and you didn't go. You now realize the reality of that spiritual movement has stopped. Your prayers will be harder, your faith will be weakened; everything becomes difficult. That is because God is calling you to come to this new level and you must respond to that.

> You risk becoming disqualified and not fulfilling the purposes for which you were created.

The position that you had been in was good enough, but now He is saying, "Come with Me." If you stay there, you will begin to wonder why things are no longer happening the way they used to. That position has become disqualified. He is moving forward and He is moving you to another place; a place that is deepening His relationship with you and increasing your mandate. He is increasing the ability and capacity of your life to fulfill His purposes.

The consequences of choosing to not go forward are devastating: the capacity you had at the former level will not be enough for God to do the things He wants to do through you. You will become a lonely soul and you will become unfulfilled, sad, and miserable. You risk becoming disqualified and not fulfilling the purposes for which you were created.

The only way to come back to the place of peace that surpasses all understanding is to seek to regain the position the Lord is bringing you into. And He is faithful; as we seek Him to help, He will faithfully do through us what we cannot do ourselves, and He will lead us into that deeper level of trust and faith, into that deeper position that He is calling us into.

> "I am the true vine, and my Father is the gardener. He cuts off every branch in me that bears no fruit, while every branch that does bear fruit he prunes so that it will be even more fruitful. You are already clean because of the word I have spoken to you. Remain in me, and I will remain in you. No branch can bear fruit by itself; it must remain in the vine. Neither can you bear fruit unless you remain in me. I am the vine; you are the branches. If a man remains in me and I in him, he will bear much fruit; apart from me you can do nothing. If anyone does not remain in me, he is like a branch that is thrown away and withers; such branches are picked up, thrown into the fire and burned. If you remain in me and my words remain in you, ask whatever you wish, and it will be given you. This is to my Father's glory, that you bear much fruit, showing yourselves to be my disciples."
>
> John 15:1-8

▶ Exercise:

Read John 15:1-8. What does Jesus say we must do to stay in position with Him? ______________________________

____

____

If we stay in this position with Jesus, what are the results? ____________

____

____

If we do not stay in this position with Jesus, what are the consequences?

____

____

____

Jesus said that we are to remain in Him. If we do, He will remain in us. We will be able to ask whatever we wish and it will be given to us. We will also bear much fruit for Him, which will glorify the Lord and show the world that we are His disciples. If we do not remain in our covenantal position with Him, we will be cut off from Him. And He warns that without Him, we can do nothing. Remaining in Christ enables us to do the works that God requires of us; stepping out of that position disqualifies us and we become unable to fulfill that purpose for which we were created.

A Warning

Praying into mandate is a position of power. When you are in that position, you rest in God, you cast away all fears and anxieties. In that position you know that all things are possible. You are walking in obedience to His instructions and commands. It is in that place where God begins to use you to accomplish His purposes in powerful ways. And as long as you stay in that position, the right atmospheric environment begins to attract His presence.

▸ **Exercise:**

Fill in the components of mandate in the diagram below:

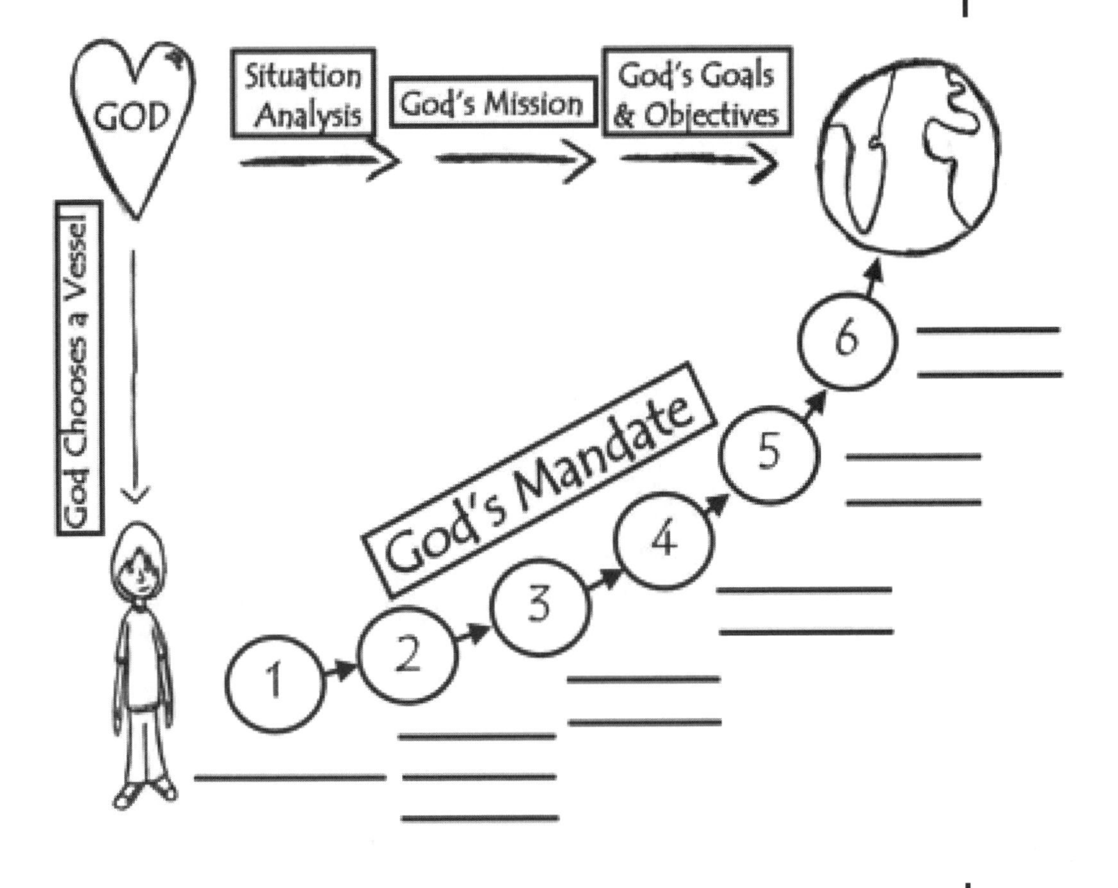

In your own words, what is the position of mandate? ______________________

____

____

____

Be aware that the enemy knows what it means for you to be in full position, and he is going to fight you as hard as he can to try to knock you out of position. He will try to distract you, to divert your attention, to scare you, to offend you, to make circumstances that take away your focus from that position; he will do whatever he can to steal, kill, and destroy our standing, fully believing and yielded to the Lord.

This is a position that we must fight for. We must face this battle and overcome the enemy. Being in position is essential for us to be able to overcome the warfare that will come against us, to fulfill the mandate that God has given us, and to attract the presence of the Holy Spirit.

Summary

What is the secret to a heart prepared for the Holy Spirit? It is positioning: "Remain in me, and I will remain in you." Remain in your full position: abide in Christ as He abides in you. Allow the Lord to create in your heart an atmosphere in which He can and will work, and through which you can attract His Spirit.

Time for Reflection:

What is the most meaningful statement or scripture you read today? ______________________________

What does God want you to do in response to this? ______________________________

As you pray your prayer target for this day/week, what are you feeling the Holy Spirit is saying or calling you to and what is the warfare coming against you? ______________________________

▸ Prayer Time:

Pray deeper into the Lord's presence, seeking God for a heart that wants Him and His purposes more than anything or anyone.

Lesson 3.

The Atmosphere Around Us

At one time in Uganda, the Lord began to speak to the church, saying, "I want to start moving in this nation, but I want you to start with your homes. Draw My presence into your homes in such a strong way that people will walk in and sense my presence and My peace. Guests who sleep in your homes will wake up in the morning and begin to confess their sins." And He promised, "When you worship Me in your homes I will come down and I will manifest Myself to you."

The whole concept of prayer altars was to start in the home. Why? Because God wanted to work in the nation of Uganda. He wanted to take the nation into His destiny, to change and transform it. But He started by saying, "You are the ones I am going to use. Create an atmosphere for My presence."

God was showing them the way to create the atmosphere that would attract His presence. In that environment, God would begin to reveal Himself; to reveal His mission and give direction, instructions, requirements, gifts, promises, etc; and to begin to mold the people in ways He wanted them to be in order to do His work.

We began realizing that we wanted to create this atmosphere that draws the Holy Spirit in the environment around us, and one of the first places we knew we needed to start was in our homes. We have been doing this in many places around the world, and we've heard so many testimonies that we could fill this book; we'll share one below.

Testimony

A single mother living in the United States had three children; two were teenagers and one was in elementary school. One of the two older children was being drawn into sexual sin; the other was being drawn into deep worldliness. The third one was angry and getting in a lot of trouble at school, such as suspensions, etc. The mother was a prayer leader. When she heard the teaching of World Trumpet Mission, she began to say, "I want to draw the presence of God into my home. I've tried everything I know; I don't know how to straighten out my children. I've tried reasoning; I've tried sharing scriptures; I've tried everything." So she began to pray every day, establishing an altar (which we will discuss in later lessons) to draw the presence of God.

As she began praying, going through her hopelessness, her fear, her condemnation, her discouragement, and was really focusing on Christ, His presence began to come and rise up her faith. In the midst of that, He began to say, "Call these two other people to start praying with you." They joined with her to start praying, and within about 1 month, the presence of God began to draw her children. One of her oldest children began to come and pray with them, then the second one, then the third. And the Presence began to affect them; it was almost like scales falling from their eyes and hardness beginning to fall from their heart.

God then began to break through and expose things that were going on, sins began to be confessed and repented of. The things they desired began to change. The children began to share that they had more desire for God than they ever had. They started to read their Bible, to go to church, to begin to seek and follow God. Within a period of 2 months, the whole atmosphere of that home had changed and the children's hearts were turned back to the Lord. They even began to make choices and decisions that were about seeking God instead of running away from God.

This continued to build so much that within 3 months, other people started to call and ask if they could join the prayer that was going on; about 20 people were eventually coming to the time of prayer. This was all the result of drawing the presence of God into the home.

he Importance of the Presence of the Holy Spirit

In the beginning, the first thing God required was to have the presence of the Holy Spirit covering the entire surface of the earth. He then spoke His word and the word brought creation into being (Genesis 1:1-4).

When the Holy Spirit is present, the word of God takes on an ability to bring forth things in a way that it didn't before. For example, when the angel Gabriel told Mary that she was going to become pregnant, she asked, "How will this be since I am a virgin?" What was the angel's answer? "The Holy Spirit will come upon you" (Luke 1:34-35).

Do you hear the principle? "The Spirit of God will come upon you and you will conceive." Why? Because there is no word that comes from the mouth of the Lord that is void of power.

▶ Exercise

We need to be aware, however, that outside the atmosphere of the Holy Spirit, things can be made powerless. Read the following scriptures. What do they say about the word of God?

Mark 7:9-13: ____

____

____

Hebrews 4:12: ____

____

____

Hebrews 1:3: ____

____

____

In Mark 7:9-13, Jesus said to the Jews, "You have made the word of God powerless by your traditions." Because of the traditions they had adopted, the Jews had created an environment where even the word of God could not do what it is supposed to do. But Hebrews 4:12 says "the word of God is living and active," and Hebrews 1:3 says that the word of God is so powerful that it sustains all things. We need to realize that there are things we can do to render the word of God powerless.

How do we see this in our own day and time? ______________________

____

____

As you ponder these, think about the state of things today. Why does it seem like the word of God is almost ineffective? It is having no effect in our cities, our nations, our neighborhoods, and many times even our churches. It doesn't seem to have the power to do what it is supposed to do. Yet, in Isaiah 55:10-11, God says, "For as the rain comes down, and the snow from heaven, and do not return there, but water the earth, and make it bring forth and bud, that it may give seed to the sower and bread to the eater, so shall my word be that goes forth from my mouth; it shall not return to me void, but it shall accomplish what I please, and it shall prosper in the thing for which I sent it" (NKJV).

▶ Exercise:

In your own words, how vital is it that we create an atmosphere that draws the presence of the Holy Spirit? ______________________

____

____

There is no word that comes from the mouth of God that lacks power, but it needs an atmosphere in which to operate. Even with Mary, with all the desire of the Father to make His word come about, the Spirit of God had to be present first.

The Results of Creating an Environment in Which God Will Work

Part of the work of bringing change to others is not only in seeking the anointing to come upon you so that the words have power when you speak; it is also in seeking the Lord for the ability to push back darkness in order to create an environment filled with the presence of God. Once such an environment is created, the word will be able to start working.

For example, those who are called into the ministry of preaching must not only prepare their lives, they have to prepare the spiritual environment. Then, when people gather to hear the word, not only will it have impact on their lives, the atmosphere filled with the Holy Spirit will also challenge them and empower the word that is spoken.

This principle is very important to understand if we are going to be successful as agents of change in our homes, churches, or communities. It is also why, traditionally, evangelists would send people into a city and ask for prayer. They would ask the churches to raise up intercession for the coming crusade. And once the venue was identified, they would ask the intercessors to go on site and pray in order to prepare the ground and draw the presence of God.

In the revival that has taken place in Argentina in the past few decades, thousands of intercessors would pray on the grounds of the venue for several days before the crusade began. Evangelists like Carlos Annacondia would even have their platform built very high so that intercessors could be praying underneath during the crusade. Before, during, and after the crusade, there would be prayer, calling down the presence of God

This is a principle we need to remember even as we prepare for a Sunday service. Simply having people come into our services and having a good message is not enough. There is no power in our words. We need to be come in earlier and pray, breaking the influence of darkness and attracting the presence of the Holy Spirit so that by the time the people begin to come, they will be walking into the presence of God. Even before the word of God comes, the Spirit will be at work.

Jesus said that when the Holy Spirit comes, He will convict the world of sin, righteousness, and judgment (John 16:5-11). So, even before the preacher begins to speak, we must draw His Presence. Sadly, this is something that we often neglect today.

Another example of preparing for crusades is Kathryn Kuhlman. Not only would intercessors pray at the venue several days before the crusade began, but they also would pray through the buses that would be used to bring people from different cities to the meetings. There are testimonies of people walking onto the buses and beginning to cry out and repent; sometimes they were even healed. There was no worship or preacher, only the presence of the Holy Spirit.

Preparing the Ground

It is vital that we have a clear understanding of the importance of the presence of the Holy Spirit. Intercessors who don't have this understanding will pray for every other detail and be satisfied that they prayed before the meeting.

Those who appreciate the importance of the presence of the Lord will cry out, examine their hearts, repent of anything that would repel the Holy Spirit, and do whatever needs to be done until the Presence comes.

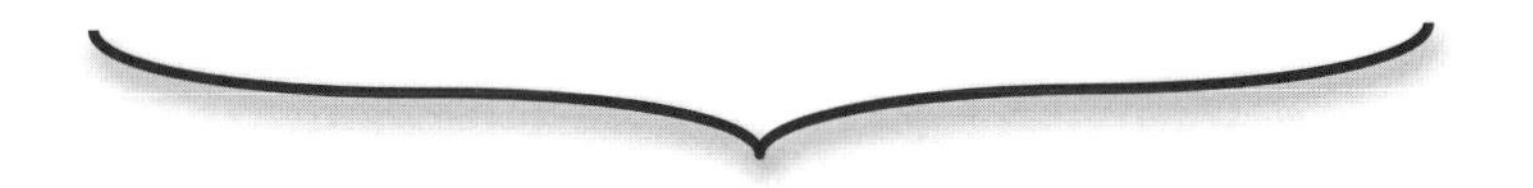

Jesus said that apart from Him, we cannot do anything. We need to come back to the place where we realize that it is not just our human preaching, our organization, or our methods or strategies that we need; we desperately need His presence. There needs to be an urgency that rises up within us to make us desperate for Him to come and move in our midst. As that desperation begins to build, we need to be willing to do anything that He asks of us, anything that needs to be done, because we know that we will never begin to make any progress without His presence.

> We are not lacking activity; we are lacking His presence.

There needs to be a cry that begins to resound within us and that grows louder and louder and louder in our churches, in our prayer groups, and even in our own hearts. This is a desperate crying out, knowing that we must be heard. We must draw His presence, no matter what it takes.

When the Presence comes, we'll know it. We'll be ready for God to start working. At that point, His work can begin to go forward; nothing will be impossible, and we will begin to see Him do things only God can do.

▶ Exercise:

When we rely on our own human abilities, what are the results we see? ___

____

____

If we draw the presence of God, what are the promised results? _________

____

____

Beloved, we must begin to hunger for His presence and begin to do whatever it takes to draw the presence of God. We are not lacking activity; we are lacking His presence.

Time for Reflection:

What is the most meaningful statement or scripture you read today? _______________

____

What does God want you to do in response to this? _______________

____

As you pray your prayer target for this day/week, what are you feeling the Holy Spirit is saying or calling you to and what is the warfare coming against you? _______________

____

▶ Prayer Time:

Continue to press into the Lord, seeking to draw His presence to the environment around you.

Lesson 4.
The System of Life Around Us

As we become revival carriers, vessels God is going to use to accomplish His mission, we need to be aware of how to allow the Holy Spirit to gain influence not only inside of us (in our lives), but also in our surroundings (in our homes, neighborhoods, congregations, and cities). We need to know how to fight and push back the darkness, not only in our own lives but also in our environment, which includes the five basic elements of society that we have already discussed.

▶ Exercise:

List the five elements of society (*see* week 3, lesson 2):

1. ______________________________
2. ______________________________
3. ______________________________
4. ______________________________
5. ______________________________

All five of these elements of society (government, worship, family, economic system, and belief system) were intended for man. For example, it was God who created man to rule. That means that God has a concept of government and leadership that is kingdom-based. And God said that a man would leave his father and mother and be united to his wife (Genesis 2:24), meaning that He has a concept for the institute of marriage. God instituted not only government and family, but the scriptures are full of His direction about how we are to worship, what we are to believe, and how we are to work and do business as well. We can therefore trust that if the Holy Spirit is allowed to guide things in all five of these areas, He will guide them God's way.

Drawing the Presence to Our Land

Sometimes, some of us feel more faith to pray for our lives, our family, or even our churches, but when we begin to pray for bigger things we get intimated and can shrink back. We can feel like we cannot make a difference in such a large thing. It is true that in human power and human ability, we are incapable of making a great difference a vast majority of the time; but we are not talking about human power, we are talking about the power of God. We are talking about the church awakening and rising up, and seeing that we must begin to take responsibility to push back the darkness in our land. We are also seeing that we are going to need others to do this, and will join with others to pray for God's Spirit to move in the surroundings of our nations and cities.

Testimony

I didn't have the faith to believe that God could move in a large-scale territory. I had no experience of something of that magnitude happening before, but my church began crying out for God to move in our city. We wanted Him to make a way for impact in our community, to see Him move and begin to affect our surroundings.

We had learned to wait on God and not just do things in our human strength, so we began to cry out for Him to show us the way forward. Within a few months, the Orlando Police Department sent out an invitation for churches to come together for 40 days of prayer and fasting for Parramore, an area in Orlando with the highest crime rates. We knew this was God at work and joined with over 70 other churches in daily prayer for this area.

During the 40 days of prayer, good news reports started to come. The worst criminals started to get arrested (one turned himself in), crime rates were dramatically reduced; the police were perplexed at the sudden drop in crime. The Mayor of the city recognized that prayer was having an impact, and Fox News came and did a national report. Police departments from other cities started to contact us and the Orlando Police Department to see how to do the same thing in their city. The Police Department recognized our church, saying we had made a difference in our city. There was even a headline in the newspaper declaring that "Prayer Is Changing Orlando."

God answered our prayers as we joined with other churches and cried out to see God move, and has even begun to get us involved with other police departments in other cities and countries. Needless to say, we now know without a doubt that God can move in the sectors of our society.

—Pastor Mark Daniel

We can affect our surroundings, especially when we join with other parts of the body of Christ to create an atmosphere full of the Holy Spirit and to push back the darkness. Let's look at ways we can begin to influence these spheres. We will mention two of them.

Government. Let's look at God's concept of government. God called David the shepherd of His people (Psalm 78:70-72). So to God, government and leadership is similar to shepherding. A shepherd loves the sheep, takes care of them, is fair to all of them, risks his life for them, and will fight to defend them. If one gets lost, he will go out to look for it and bring it back to join the others. That is kingdom-based government; that is leadership God's way.

▶ **Exercise:**

Read 1 Samuel 8:4-18.

What did God warn the people would happen if they had a king to reign over them? ____

____

____

God warned the people that a king would tax them, make their sons serve in his army and their daughters serve in his kitchens; that he would take their fields and produce, a tenth of their harvest and their flocks, and their servants and animals for his own use. He would even bring them into slavery. God was trying to warn them that a king following the world's idea of government and leadership would not take care for them the way that He would.

God will give us leaders who will thrive in the atmosphere we create. That means we can begin to influence the type of political leaders we shall have tomorrow. Let us pray then for leaders in our cities and nations who will govern and lead according to God's concepts; who have shepherd's hearts and a desire to care for the people. Let us ask Him to give us men or women with the heart of a shepherd to represent us in Parliament, to represent us in the city counsel, to be our President. Leaders who will love and shepherd the people they lead, and who will create systems that protect, serve, and strengthen the people.

If we are crying out for transformation in our cities and nations, we must make this a part of what we are praying. We must pray that God will touch each of these elements of society and bring them under His control. If the atmosphere over leadership is under the control of the Holy Spirit, God will give us men and women who He considers proper leaders. Likewise, if God is given control over families, worship, the economy, and the people's belief system, it will create an environment in which the Holy Spirit will be able to work.

Every act of worship connects the physical world with the spiritual world.

Worship. Worship is the ability of man to connect with his god. Man was created to worship, and since it is innate within us, we will worship something, whether it is a false god, things of man (money, sports, hobbies, etc), or the one true living God. Every act of worship connects the physical world with the spiritual world.

Brothers and sisters, we are all priests. When we worship or perform a religious activity, we are building a bridge between our physical world and the spiritual world. We are connecting these two realms with the idea that we shall draw from the spiritual into the physical. We don't see God in every act of worship or religious activity that we do, whether it is prayer or worship, but we have faith that we are touching God's presence and connecting with the spiritual realm.

For example, when you tithe, you bring our offering in the physical world, put it in a physical container, and give it to a physical minister of God believing that somehow and somewhere there will be a connection with God, who is going to bless you. It is not the minister who will give it back to you multiplied, it is not the minister who is going to bless you. No. You are connecting to the spiritual world in this act of giving and are expecting that something is going to come back to you. Why? Because you believe that what you are doing is not just in the physical world; you are connecting with the spiritual world.

Remember when Solomon gave his sacrifice in the temple? When he finished praying, the spiritual world came down so strongly that even the priests could not minister (2 Chronicles 7:1-2). We can therefore see that worship, prayer, and religious activities connect the physical world to the spiritual world.

▸ **Exercise:**

What are people in our society worshiping? ______________________

____

____

What impact is that having on the physical world? ____________________

____

____

How can we begin to pray for God to bring a change in who is controlling the spiritual world? ____________________

____

____

An Atmosphere of Darkness

Just as we who are called by His name can connect to God, in the same way, there are people who connect to the spirit world and draw the presence of darkness. And just as God can overwhelm people, this dark power can also overwhelm people. When the presence of darkness envelops an area, even people who haven't planned on doing evil are overtaken. They end up going the wrong way and doing things they would never have thought of doing. Sometimes people will ask, "Why did you do that?" and they have no answer; it's the spiritual atmosphere of darkness.

Just as God requires a spiritual atmosphere in which to work, so does the devil. And just as the Father is always at work, so is the devil; he is at work to steal, kill, and destroy.

This is where it becomes very important to understand who rules the religious atmosphere in a city. We may have churches in an area, but are they influencing the spiritual atmosphere in the land? Are the unholy priests attracting more darkness in the land than the holy priests are attracting the presence of God?

▶ **Exercise:**

In your own city, what would the answer be? ____________________

____

____

There are unholy priests and altars all over the world, and they attract the presence of darkness. Abortion clinics, for example; without a doubt, they attract darkness because every time you spill blood unrighteously, you are attracting the presence of darkness. Another example is cities like New Orleans, where you can feel the darkness so dense in the air. You feel the spirit of "going wild," letting go of control. It is like a spirit of lust, a spirit of craving for things you would normally never do. If you are spiritually sensitive, you can tell immediately that this is the spiritual atmosphere that draws people from other parts of the world and other parts of America to come and "let their hair down." To do what they want, to go wild and "party. "

This is not an atmosphere in which God will work. God instructs throughout the Bible, "When you find the idols the people are worshiping, destroy them. Do not bring them into your houses. Do not even take the gold and the silver you find on them. It will turn your houses into abominations or bring a curse upon you." He says that even bringing an idol into the house is like opening a door and inviting the flood of darkness (Deuteronomy 7:25-26). When we begin to understand these things, we begin to realize that we need to watch over our houses more.

▶ Exercise:

Read Joshua 7.

What happened to the Israelites in this chapter? ______________________

____

____

Why did God say that this would occur? ______________________________

____

____

Achan brought something into his house that he was not supposed to bring. The next day Israel went to war and was defeated. When Joshua cried to God, the Lord explained, "Israel has sinned; they have violated my covenant, which I commanded them to keep. They have taken some of the devoted things; they have stolen, they have lied, they have put them with their own possessions. That is why the Israelites cannot stand against their enemies; they turn their backs and run because they have been made liable to destruction. I will not be with you anymore unless you destroy whatever among you is devoted to destruction." Do you hear what God said? "I cannot go with you." This was not the right atmosphere. As can be seen from this scripture, there are times when God says, "I'm sorry. I can't go with you. You've created an atmosphere that I cannot associate with."

A Testimony From Uganda

In recent years, the church of Uganda was faced with a challenge that was brought to them by the government, which had been fighting a rebel movement in the northern part of the nation for about 20 years. The rebels were murdering and killing, abducting young children and taking them to Sudan, taking girls as sex slaves, boys as murder machines, and women as workers to grow their food. It was very, very cruel. The American government came openly and offered to help, give weapons, training, and other things, as did the British and German governments, but the war was not going away.

One time we were gathered together to seek the Lord and lots of testimonies of transformation were being shared from all over the country. A man from the north stood up and asked, "If you are seeing communities changing within a few months when you seek God, can someone explain why we have prayed for 17 years and God does not seem to answer us? Is God a respecter of persons?" This was a challenge that we first answered with human solutions. Then, recognizing that God is not a liar, we humbled ourselves and came before God saying, "If we are praying this long and You are not answering, then something must be missing."

As we humbled ourselves we felt led to call a national fast, so we consulted with various prayer movements and church faith camps. One thing led to another and God told us, "Declare war on the spirit of witchcraft and idolatry." We did that with our little understanding. But at that same time, God spoke to a man in the army who was one of the commanders fighting against the rebels. He is born again. The Lord told him, "Tell your leaders you will never win this war with a gun. Unless you humble yourselves and pray, this war is never going to end." He passed on the word until it came to the president, who gave permission for a major prayer rally to be held in Gulu, a city in the north, which was the worst-hit area.

Some of the born-again commanders who were organizing the rally approached the church, asking them to help; the prayer meeting ended up being right in the middle of the month-long national fast. We sent different teams of pastors and intercessors over a weekend. People came in huge numbers, which was unusual, but the first 2 days were fruitless. On the second day, the Lord gave a prophetic word and said that to break the war, they had to come against the unholy altars in the land that were being used by the rebels. One of the pastors from the north began to talk to the people, who began to report back details of the altars of the enemy. There were about 17 altars the rebels used for sacrifices, including both human and animal sacrifices, and to perform rituals and draw spiritual power.

The local pastor began speaking to the people in the area and laid out what was happening. There was such a spirit of conviction that thousands of people gave their life to the Lord Jesus, including some rebels. They surrendered their witchcraft and confirmed where their altars, those unholy altars, were. We knew from this that God wanted us to go in and destroy the altars, but all these altars were in places that were war zones where only the army and the rebels could go.

However, when God directs and says, "Do this" and you do it in obedience, He knows how to open the way. The following morning was a Monday and the pastors got a message that the President was in town and he wanted them to know that he was very appreciative. He asked if one of them could meet with him. The President expressed his gratitude and asked if the pastors would continue. But the pastor said, "Sir, you don't understand. There is another war parallel to what you are fighting and you don't have the weapons to fight it. This is a spiritual war."

The pastor began to talk to the President about spiritual warfare, about the power of altars, the occult and the witchcraft that was behind the rebellion, and at some point the President gave an order for all the commanders to come in to listen. At the end of the discussion, the President said, "We will do anything you tell us to do if you assure us that the church has got power to break this thing." The pastor told the President that intercessors needed to go into the war zone to each of those altars, to pray there, to break the power, and to cleanse the land. The President agreed and offered the assistance of the army and the air force. He made helicopters and armored carriers available for them to go in to do the work.

While the pastor was telling the others about the meeting, he got a phone call from the state house; the President was asking for the pastors' strategy. He wanted us to start, to seek God and bring them a strategy, which they would implement.

We asked for a week and began praying, fasting, and waiting on the Lord. The Lord gave us specific things that needed to be done. A few weeks down the road the teams went out. The army was faithful. They provided everything. It was like war, but the soldiers were the intercessors. They were the ones going in to do war. They were going in from altar to altar to altar. They prayed in every area.

One of the top rebel leaders who later surrendered gave testimony that at that time, the rebel commander told them, "Something has happened; our power has been broken." He said the spirits have left and they will not come back. They asked him how that was possible and he said, "I don't know. I don't understand, but it is some group of Christians that is responsible for this."

From that time onwards, every ambush the rebel set up was defeated. The war that had lasted 17 years ended in the next 3 years. The government of Sudan, who was supporting the rebels, suddenly had a change of heart and decided to stop giving them support. They invited the government to send troops into its territory to pursue the rebels, which enabled thousands of women and children who had been abducted to be brought back to Uganda. The Sudanese army warned the rebels in southern Sudan to leave. After some attacks the rebels left and went into the Congo, where they were for several months. They asked for peace talks. The three governments who were involved in the peace talks—Congo, Uganda, and Sudan—united, put their forces together, and dispatched the rebel army.

What I want to bring out here is that God is able to do exceedingly, abundantly above what we can ask (Ephesians 3:20). For 17 years we thought we knew how to pray. For 17 years we thought we were doing the right thing, until that pastor challenged us: "Is God a respecter of persons? Listen to all the transformation stories you are sharing. None of them has taken more than a year or two. You pray for specific cities and God moves. You pray for specific districts and God moves. Why isn't He moving in our area? Why can't someone help me to understand?" And none of us had an answer.

But we received grace to humble ourselves before God and begin to ask what it was that we were missing, what it was that we may not be doing right. One thing led to another until a very clear strategy was put before us. And in a short time, in 3 years, the rebellion is over. Today, the people in the north who were in internally displaced people's camps are going back to their land and rebuilding their houses, hospitals, schools and other infrastructure. For the first time in 20 years, the people in that region know peace.

Changing the atmosphere to attract the presence of the Holy Spirit is an important part of the process of transforming territories. In any of the elements of society, we can choose to submit to our ways, to the ways of our society, or we can begin to allow the Holy Spirit to remind us and teach us the ways of God. Some examples are the ways we conduct our courtships, marriages, parenting, and households are not the ways of God; they are the ways of our society. The compromises that we have become accustomed to are affecting the atmosphere, and as we begin to humble ourselves and seek God, He will begin to show us those compromises. If we allow Him to cleanse us of them, we will begin to see His presence grow stronger and greater.

God says in Genesis 18:19, "I commanded Abraham to teach his children and his household to walk in my ways by doing what is right and just, so that I may fulfill the promise I made to him." What is God saying? "I can't just fulfill because I promised. Give me the right atmosphere. Raise up your children and your household in my ways. Let them do what is right and what is just, then I will come and fulfill what I promised."

In the church today, we have given up on these five areas of society because we've not known what to do. In many ways, we have tried to change them in human power. But as the church awakens, we begin to seek God and trust Him to begin to move, open doors, and transform these five spheres of society. Instead of sitting back and giving in to defeat, we begin to rise up and know that our God can begin to transform one step at a time.

Many times, as we begin to have an impact on the atmosphere, God will rise up a person in the different spheres who will be a forerunner to see transformation comes in these areas. We have seen this in many nations across the world.

CONCLUSION

As we pray into the mandate, capture the vision of God's heart, and see the urgency of the hour; as we begin to hold onto and understand the commissioning that God has given us and to rise up in our covenantal position with our lives abandoned and yielded to Him; as He begins to give us instructions and we are standing on His promises and gifts, holding onto His grace, we will be able to start changing the atmosphere around us. As we begin to come together with other believers to pray for these spheres of society, we will see the church rising up in power. It will not be through the power of human effort, but by the power of the Holy Spirit. It will not just be the words of rhetoric in the streets, but it will be the words of God that begins to awaken and stir the hearts of people, and to cause people to want to come to Him.

We will begin to see city officials, civic leaders, and others in different spheres of society beginning to have dreams at night, to understand why God placed them in a particular sphere of society. We will begin to see God uniting and bringing the church together to function as one, and have an impact over these things.

We may feel in the beginning that the change is small, but as we continue to pray into this mandate and into changing the atmospheres of our hearts, our surroundings, and the spheres of society, we will find that nothing is impossible for our God and that He is the same God yesterday, today, and tomorrow. And just as He turned cities upside down in Bible times, He will continue turning cities and nations upside down in our time.

Time for Reflection:

What is the most meaningful statement or scripture you read today? ______________________________

What does God want you to do in response to this? ______________________________

As you pray your prayer target for this day/week, what are you feeling the Holy Spirit is saying or calling you to and what is the warfare coming against you? ______________________________

▸ Prayer Time:

Spend time going deeper with the Lord; as you draw closer to Him, He will draw closer to you. Ask the Holy Spirit to teach you how to push back the darkness and to give you the strength to stand against the dark forces that want to push us back and pull us down. Praise Him that He is willing to prepare us to be part of the army that He is raising up.

Notes

Week 7.

The Way Forward

> **GOAL OF THE WEEK:**
>
> This week we want to
> 1. That even as this study is ending, you commit to continuing a daily walk with God that will continually bring you closer to fulfilling the destiny for which you were created.
> 2. That you commit to lifestyle changes that will equip you, strengthen you, and prepare you to be an active and effective member of the army of God.

In our final week of study, we want to present practical ways we can begin to walk out the things that God has shown us during the past 6 weeks. We have come to understand the process by which God thinks, the mission that He has been on throughout the ages, the mandate that He gives His chosen vessel that enables him to accomplish that mission, and we have asked and answered a few vital questions:

- What is ministry? Are we doing ministry our way or God's way?
- What is God's heart desire? What is the vision of His heart?
- What has God commissioned me to do in order to see His heart's desires fulfilled? Am I fulfilling that mission?
- *How do we work the works that God requires of us?*

In these next lessons, we will look at three specific action steps that we can take to change our lifestyle so we can begin to be about the Father's work. We are going to look at actions we can take on a personal level, actions we can take on a regional level, actions we can take to prepare ourselves for when God begins to open things up, and actions we can take to be continually growing and developing as vessels willing to be used by God to accomplish His work. At the end of the week, you will have an opportunity to make a commitment in each of these areas.

Please prayerfully prepare your heart for this week's lessons. As we mentioned in the beginning of this study, we do not want this to be just another nice study that has no impact. This study is intended to provoke, to stir, to awaken, and to call God's army to arise and go out to disciple the nations, and we trust that as you've made it this far, you already have these things stirring in your hearts.

At the end of each day's lesson, we have provided some action points that will help you take hold of the things that you have learned. We pray that these will become lifestyle changes that will strengthen and equip you as you fulfill the commission that you have been given.

At the end of this week's lessons, we have provided a way to respond to the things God revealed to you these past weeks. We will make a plea for you to commit to rise up and "take hold of that for which Christ took hold of you"; a sort of "enlistment process," if you will.

God is calling His army to rise up and take its place; will you respond and become part of that noble company of men and women who will advance the purposes of God in these last days?

Prayer targets for week 7:

1. That you would respond to what God is revealing to you through these lessons.
2. That you will catch the vision of the global army and have a desire to be part of it.

Audio/video link for week 7:

http://worldtrumpet.org/awakening-the-church (week 7)

Lesson 1.

A Personal Lifestyle Change – Maintaining a Sense of Urgency

The Time is Short

We have spoken many times in the past few weeks about the approaching Day of the Lord. We know without doubt that time is short and that we are in the last days; this should give us a sense of urgency.

The Day of the Lord is referred to three different ways in scripture. What we are referring to in this section is that season of time described throughout the Bible when the waves of darkness are beginning to build and increase. The church is called to rise up and stand against this darkness. We believe this study has shown that the season is near.

There are two things that we must acknowledge and that should provoke us to cry out to the Lord to enable us to fulfill His mission and the mandate He has given us. The first of these is that the Day of the Lord is a set date. It is not a date that we are going to determine ourselves; God has already set it. Jesus told his disciples, "No one knows about that day or hour, not even the angels in heaven, nor the Son, but only the Father" (Matthew 24:36). There is a date that has been set already, and it is drawing near.

The second is that the darkness has been growing and is coming to fullness. God cannot allow the darkness to continue to grow forever. James 1:15 says that "after desire has conceived, it gives birth to sin; and sin, when it is full-grown, gives birth to death." God cannot extend the time any further; if He does, the darkness could consume even the elect (Mark 13:20).

The Day of the Lord is a set date and it is drawing near.

We are in a time where God is saying to us, "Can't you read the signs? You cannot procrastinate forever; you need to die to everything that holds you back, to commit yourselves to the work because the time is very short." The sense of urgency, that the time is short, is not because God is making it short; it is because it is coming to its climax, to the date that has been set for it. And yet, there aren't many today who seem to have an awareness of the urgency of the hour.

Slumber

The spirit of slumber has many devastating consequences. One is that it makes us tolerant of things we know are not right, things we know are weakening us and corrupting us, but we have become compromised and even indulgent. We have gone into slumber and have begun to tolerate and accept what God finds unacceptable. We have lowered His standards.

> Slumber makes us tolerant of things we know are not right.

Other consequences are that we have lost interest in fulfilling the desires of God's heart. Our lives have become self-focused rather than God-focused. We have also lost our love for others; our hearts have grown cold and we have lost a desire to see souls saved. We are not sacrificial or generous with our love.

It is not unusual for many of us to see an alarming news report and think, "Oh my, this is terrible," and then an hour later the memory of that has been washed away. In that first moment we may think that we must see a breakthrough, but we quickly lose His heart. This is slumber.

This is a spiritual force that is coming against the earth today, and the church is getting caught up in it. It is making us ineffective, immobilized, weak, and powerless. This is where the darkness wants us to be.

Slumber is a spirit that is strong in this era in which we live. It is pushing on us and trying to steal our hope, vision, and clarity. It is trying to steal our faith, trust, courage, and perseverance. It is trying to push us back so that we don't pursue the Lord or our destiny. Slumber causes us to compromise our consecration and make things about ourselves.

This study can provoke us into a greater sense of urgency, an awareness of our mandate, and a sense of need for us to join together as an army and be about the mission of God, but there is a force coming against us that is trying to keep us from rising up. We must set our hearts to come against this spiritual force, which wants us to sit down, to lose focus, and to become complacent. We *must* get out from under this spirit of slumber, but how do we do that?

> **Two reasons why we must fight the spiritual force of slumber:**
>
> 1. Jesus told us that we must resist it or it will capture us
> 2. We must complete the work and time is growing short

Why We Must Fight Slumber. There are two reasons why we must fight the spiritual force of slumber. Both can be found in the word. The first is because Jesus told us that we must resist the pull of slumber or it will capture us. The second is that we must complete the work; the hour is growing late and the time to complete the work is growing short.

▶ **Exercise:**

Read Luke 21:34-36: "Be careful, or your hearts will be weighed down with dissipation, drunkenness and the anxieties of life, and that day will close on you unexpectedly like a trap. For it will come upon all those who live on the face of the whole earth. Be always on the watch, and pray that you may be able to escape all that is about to happen, and that you may be able to stand before the Son of Man."

What happens to your heart if you are not careful or alert? ____________

____

____

Who will face this wave? ________________________________

____

____

What does Jesus instruct us to do? ___________________________

____

____

Notice that Jesus uses the word "always." Be *always* on the watch.

We must set our hearts to come against the spiritual force of slumber, which wants us to sit down, to lose focus, and to become complacent.

Read Luke 21:34-36 again and review your answers. Imagine that you don'live in a nation where the church teaches about the Day of the Lord. People do not feel the alarm that Jesus gave and they will be caught unaware. They don't understand the gravity of the time that we are in.

Jesus does not speak in exaggerations. We must therefore take it close to heart when He tells us, "Be careful. Take heed and stay alert. Pray that you will be able to escape."

We need to remember that Jesus only spoke the words the Father gave Him. He doesn't waste words; He does not speak in exaggerations, so we must soberly take it close to heart when He tells us, "Be careful. Take heed and stay alert. Protect your hearts and be prepared. Pray that you will be able to escape, for that day will close on you unexpectedly like a trap." Jesus tells us that this will face everybody on the face of the earth, which includes us. He tells us that we must pray, that if we do not specifically come against this, it will capture us.

When Jesus tells us that we must pray about something, we need to understand that this is going to be a massive force and we must begin to strategically and specifically pray so that we will be able to escape it as well as be able to stand when it comes. This is something that is not being discussed in many Christian circles, but it is what our Lord told us to do in these last days.

The hour is growing late; the time to complete our work is growing shorter.

The Second Reason Why We Must Fight Slumber. We have seen in our study that the church has lost sight of its mission. Because of that, there are many layers of understanding that have been lost. One of those is that God intended that we finish the work that He has given us. We aren't supposed to be busy or just involved in His work; we are to see that the work is completed.

When we realize that 2,000 years have passed, the church has not fulfilled God's mission, and there is a set time coming upon us, we begin to have a sense of urgency.

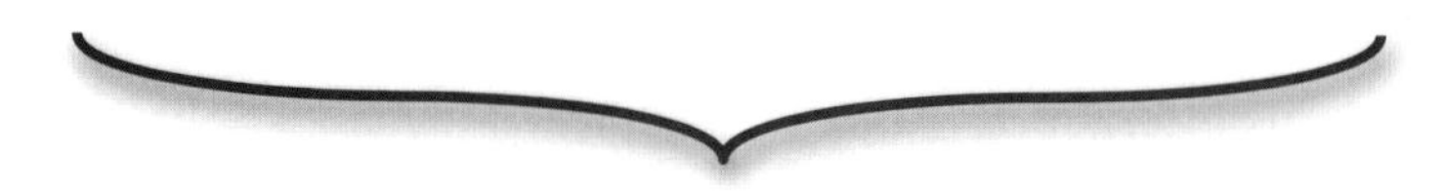

The hour is growing late; the time to complete our work is growing shorter. In the Bible, you don't find Jesus just settle with showing up or doing good activities. He said, "My food…is to do the will of him who sent me and to finish his work" (John 4:34). Jesus is focused on His mission and is about accomplishing the mission He has been given.

God has given us a responsibility to be about His purposes and instructed us to be set apart. We aren't to get caught up in the deception of slumber and the dissipation of our times. We are to stay in a state of readiness before the Lord.

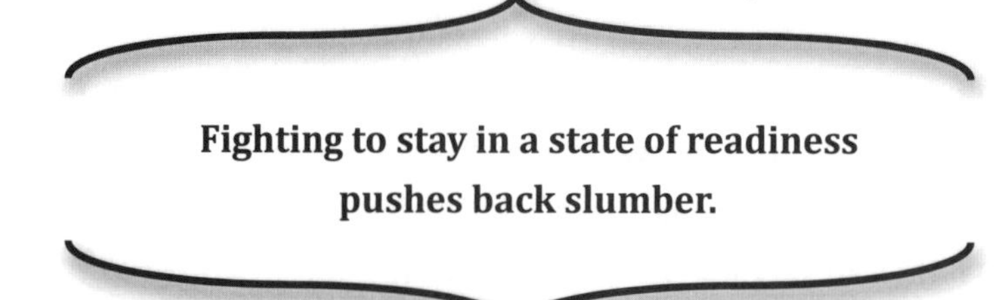

Fighting to stay in a state of readiness pushes back slumber.

The spirit of slumber will cover the whole earth. It is something the Jesus told us we must fight against or it will catch us unaware; it will begin to draw us in without us even noticing, and it will bring an attitude of heart that is compromising, that is not hungry to fulfill the mission we've been given, that seems to lack power. There is a real need to come out of this compromise, this disobedience, and this lethargy in our spirit, and to give ourselves fully to Christ.

▶ **Exercise:**

What are the two reasons why we need to fight slumber? ______________

____

____

Jesus told us that we must resist slumber or it will capture us. Also, we must complete the work that we have been given and time is growing short.

How do we fight slumber? By developing a lifestyle of saturating in God's word and hallowing the name of the Lord.

Action Points

We have found that saturating in God's Word and spending an extended time before God every day allows us to be aligned to the Bible and not the times in which we live. We learn who God is through reading the Bible and then spend time praising Him, worshiping Him, and pressing deeper into His heart. We also must pray daily into the position of mandate. This discipline helps us maintain a sense of urgency and break free of the spirit of slumber.

Saturating in the Word. We live in a day and time when so much comes at us at once; it occupies our minds, captures our hearts, and affects our perspectives and our views. We desire to rise up into the purposes of God, but there is literally no way to do that if we stay under the cloud and confusion that reigns over the nations in this day and time. Our souls are being saturated in this era, both in the increased noise of it as well as in the spiritual slumber and worldliness. The only hope for us to begin to rise out of that is for us to change the environment in which our souls are dwelling.

Our souls are being saturated in something, either in this environment that we have described, which is against the purposes of God, or in His word and His presence. It is impossible to stand against the slumber without setting aside

> "When I first read the Bible from beginning to end, reading big chunks each day, it brought me to my knees as I realized that I didn't know the God I was reading about. I read so little and so slowly before that I had never seen His fierce wrath and His love together and I couldn't comprehend this God I was supposedly following."
>
> *Clare, 32*

Testimony From Pastor Mark Daniel

Over the years, when praying with the Ugandans, I began to see that the majority of their prayers are praising the name of the Lord and drawing deeper and deeper into His presence. I realized they spent more time focusing on His purposes, while trusting that He would take care of their problems. The Ugandans challenged me, and others, to start saturating in the Word of God. They said we were to read 10 or 15 chapters of the Bible every day. This was not for Bible study – that was for another time in the day or week – this was for Bible reading, and had only one purpose: to get to know the God that is revealed in these pages.

As I began to saturate in the Word, I began believing that the more and more I read the Bible, the more and more my righteousness would increase and that I would start walking in deeper and deeper levels of faith. I believed that I was going to start thinking and seeing things more through God's perspective then from a human worldly perspective. I realized I was going to begin to understand the God that I am relating to and know His purposes and His ways, that I was going to begin to have His heart more, and that it was going to begin to affect the very way that I pray.

Since then, wherever we have encouraged people to begin to read 10 to 15 chapters of the Bible every day, the prevalent testimony from people who have given themselves to this discipline is, "Saturating in the Word has changed my life; it's changed everything." I have seen God teach and disciple people so much more in the last few years of saturating in the Word that I ever did in my previous 27 years of ministry. They read the Word of God and He's teaching them to parent, how to do marriage; He's teaching them how to deal with adversities, how to do battle, and how to pray.

at least an hour a day to allow the word of God to cover our minds and our hearts, and to reshape and redirect us.

The more we saturate in the Word of God, the more it starts separating us from the world's thinking, standards, and systems. You start realizing, for example, that our world system wants everything quick and easy. We want it fast and get discouraged when we don't get it that way. We walk away from God and feel justified when He doesn't answer us with a swift solution. When you read the whole Bible, and not just pieces, you start seeing God in the fullness of who He is.

The effect of saturating in the Word is like pulling layers of darkness, layers of the defilement of this land, layers of human thinking and layers of human ways, pulling them away day after day, month after month. After a couple of years you look back and realize you don't even think the same way you used to think, you don't look at things or operate in the same way, and you can't imagine not saturating in the Word of God. It humbles you, rebukes you, strengthens you, builds faith in you, transforms your appetites—it feeds your soul. The Word of God becomes a wall of protection around your life.

If you are going to be an agent of change and bring transformation, you need to go back to the Bible. We need to go back to reading the Bible like it is life and like it is food. And we need to allow it to change our mindsets. Remember what Jesus said? "If you hold to my teaching, you are really my disciples. Then you will know the truth, and the truth will set you free" (John 8:31-32).

Hallowing the Name of the Lord. Jesus said in the Lord's Prayer, "hallowed be your name" (Matthew 6:9, Luke 11:2). To "hallow" means to make something holy and to have great respect and reverence for somebody or something. Hallowing God's name is beginning to esteem Him, beginning to take what we read in the word of God and to ascribe to Him the worth, honor, blessing, acknowledgement, affection, trust, and fear that His name deserves. Hallowing the name of the Lord is a spiritual exercise that we are often, particularly in the West, not very good at. Reading the word is also a spiritual exercise; we need to stop trying to use our intellect and start depending on the spirit of God to take the word of God into us and feed us.

We have seen in previous weeks that humanism is one of the plagues affecting many nations of the earth in these last days. Humanism exalts man and devalues God, but as we begin to read the word of God, to really see who He is, and to intentionally, consistently, and constantly exalt Him and humble ourselves, things begin to come back in order.

We encourage people to read the Bible and then begin to hallow God from what they read in the word. Begin to acknowledge who He is, to ascribe to Him glory; begin to bless His name and His faithfulness. Many times, the more we begin to hallow His name, the nearer we move to attracting and drawing His presence down.

As people begin to hallow the name of the Lord, it will feel difficult, awkward, and strained at first. As they keep going, they will literally feel that they are pushing against a veil that is over their own lives and over their home, and as they push, they can feel that they are coming against something. They can continue to hallow God's name until a breakthrough, an opening, comes. Out of this place of breakthrough, they can go into intercession, warfare, and declaration because their prayers are then coming from a place of connecting with the Lord and not just from themselves.

We have seen this happen in many places. When the opening first begins to come, it seems small, like a little opening, but the more the people kept hallowing

> "My appetites have completely changed because of saturating in the Word. I don't know why everything changed, I can just tell you that by reading the Word it has changed."
>
> *Josh, 20*

the Lord's name day after day, the opening would grow larger, and the capacity for them to draw near to God would expand, their faith would grow, they would begin to have greater understanding and revelation, and they would begin to rise up into stronger and stronger positions in the Lord Jesus.

Hallowing the name of God is one of the ways we keep the spiritual forces of our day and time at bay. It is one of the ways we can even begin establish a place of open heavens, an opening over us where we are not getting captured by the things of our day and time.

Praying Into the Mandate. Praying daily into the position of mandate is essential to help hold onto the sense of urgency that we need to fight slumber. Below is a chart to help illustrate how this can be done:

Praying Into the Mandate

- First, pray into His commissioning and to treat as holy the calling that He's put upon your life.
- Ask Him to help you catch the vision of His heart. To understand the burdens of His heart, the seriousness and depth of what He has been doing throughout the centuries, and the season of time we are going into in the nations and the church. Begin to carry the burden that God has.
- Begin to hold up and declare your covenantal position; that you have been set apart for His purposes, that you belong to Him, and that He has called you at this time and this day. Abandon yourself to Him; trust Him and yield your life to Him, declaring that "My life is not mine; it belongs to Him." Come to a place of complete trust and submission to Him.
- Submit and yield yourself to the instructions and commands God has given you as He is molding and shaping you to be a vessel He can use.
- Hold up God's gifts and promises as the enemy comes against you and tries to intimidate you, to get you to shrink back. Hold them up as a banner, declaring what God has called you to do.
- Finally, trust the grace and anointing that God has given you to do the work: "My God's grace is sufficient to see everything through. He cannot fail. He will be faithful to complete this work."

Summary

Saturating in the word of God (10 to 15 chapters a day) and hallowing the name of the Lord bring us into an intimate knowledge of who our God is. They break us free from slumber, give us insight into God's heart desires, set our hearts on God's purposes, help us to remain alert, ready, and prepared for the day of the Lord, and so much more. They bring life and meaning into our existence. We encourage you today to begin a lifestyle of reading the Word and hallowing the name of the Lord.

Time for Reflection:

What is the most meaningful statement or scripture you read today? ______________________

What does God want you to do in response to this? ______________________

As you pray your prayer target for this day/week, what are you feeling the Holy Spirit is saying or calling you to and what is the warfare coming against you? ______________________

▶ **Prayer Time:**

The Lord instructed us to stand against the forces of our day. Begin to acknowledge that slumber is a force in our day and that we need to come into agreement with Him. Ask Him to teach you how to rise up and fight against this spiritual force.

Begin to surrender yourself to a lifestyle of a daily time in God's word, allowing it to wash over you, as well as to an extended time with Him in prayer, which begins with hallowing His name.

Lesson 2.
A Personal Lifestyle Change — Being Set Apart Unto God

All throughout this study we have been asking the question, "What must we do to do the works God requires?" When we start seeking the answer to that question, not asking God to come and bless our plans, but asking Him, "Lord, reveal Your ways, reveal Your will, reveal Your Kingdom and we will follow You," we are going to start seeing immediate results in our communities, in cities, families, and mission. Surrendering to the Lord is not something simple, and it's not something that we do and finish. It's something we continue to keep going deeper and deeper into. And the more we surrender—the more we pray into that covenantal position of trust and abandonment to the Lord—the more we see the authority and gain the faith that can change issues, not only on our family's level, but that can also effect whole cities, cultures, and even nations.

A few weeks ago, we were considering God's heart, how He analyzes a situation and plans to bring it back into alignment with His intended purposes. In every era in history, when God chose to intervene in the affairs of humanity, He called someone out of their surroundings and separated them from the mindsets, customs, and ways that life of that era. He would set them apart unto Himself so that He could prepare them to be a vessel through which He could work.

The Need to be Set Apart

None of us can be an instrument of revival in our generation or in our land unless we are willing to let God set us apart. We don't realize how much of our nation's thinking, ways, mindsets, concepts, and perspective have colored, affected, shaped, and molded us. We may not understand how deep He needs to go within us or all that He needs to change, but He is calling us to say, "I'm letting go and will follow you; I'm going to do what You ask of me."

God is the only one who can prepare me and make me a vessel useful for His purposes.

We have to let go of control and stop trying to map things out ourselves. We have to let God take us where we could never go on our own. He knows how to expose every idolatrous place in our hearts, every place where we do not trust or believe Him and where we do not abide in Him or obey Him. He knows how to strip away everything that hinders us from fulfilling this work, and He knows how to build everything within us so that we can carry the work that is in front of us. We must abandon ourselves and allow Him to do this work.

Many times people have the desire to see transforming revival, but they don't see how to go forward. They do everything they know how to do and everything they have seen or heard anybody else doing, but nothing breaks through. The reason is that they are not allowing God to prepare them to be a vessel He can use. They aren't allowing Him to set them apart.

We have no ability to break through the system of our culture and our world unless we allow God to break through that in us and then raise us up above it. Once we allow God to do that, we begin to have the understanding, authority, and faith needed to be able to come against the things that are holding our nations captive.

▶ Exercise:

Read 1 Samuel 2:12-36. Describe what is happening when the people come to make their sacrifices. ______________________________

____

____

The sons of Eli, the high priest, were wicked men. They were priests, but they had no regard for the Lord and treated His offerings with contempt. Even before the fat was burned, which was a requirement of God, the servant of the priest would come and say to the men who were sacrificing, "Give the priest some meat to roast; he won't accept boiled meat from you, only raw." Look at how defiled the land was. In his old age, Eli heard about the wickedness and everything his sons were doing, and he reproved them. But they did not listen to his rebuke because the Lord had determined to put them to death. In the midst of this evil, God began to establish someone who could prepare the land. The scriptures say that Samuel was ministering before the Lord; he grew up in the presence of the Lord, and he grew in stature and in favor with the Lord and with men.

Do you notice that these verses describe the darkness in the land? But they also keep saying things like, "But Samuel was in the presence of God." The corruption in the land had gotten so great that the priests were able to make offerings in contempt.

Imagine going to church to worship; you've got burdens and you're coming to pray, wanting to bow down and turn to God and ask him for help. That's what the altar was during Eli's time: the place of giving your offering to be right with God, to ask him to deal with your burdens. But the priests, the men of God, come in and treat this with contempt. What would that do to your prayer, to your request, to the burdens that you carry? Do you go away with faith knowing that God has heard you? No! The priests are just treating them with force. They are being immoral and therefore open up more immorality all over the land. It is affecting the land deeply. But all along, Samuel was growing in the presence of God; he stayed in the presence of God.

A man of God spoke the word of the Lord to Eli, laying before him the calling he and his fathers had, and then declaring the Lord's intent to cut short his and his descendants' strength because he had despised that calling and dishonored the name of the Lord. The man of God prophesied of the impending disaster coming on Eli and his sons, and the promise to raise up a faithful priest who will do all that is in God's heart and mind (1 Samuel 2:27-36).

These were dark times, not unlike our own. There was much corruption, even in the house of the Lord, and they were treating holy things like they were common. The Bible says the word of the Lord was scarce (1 Samuel 3:1), so what were they preaching? They were not preaching the word of the Lord, so their words did not have life, did not have the power to break through. There was not even the strength to repent much in that day. Even when Eli was told of the judgment, he said, "He is the Lord; let him do what is good in his eyes" (1 Samuel 3:18). Even the wicked king Ahab ripped his garments, threw dust on his head, and began to cry out for mercy when he received judgment from the Lord (1 Kings 21:27), but Eli didn't even have the strength to repent: "Just let the Lord do what He's going to do." These were low, dark times. Can you imagine this kind of environment?

How is it that Samuel wasn't corrupted by his surroundings? He stayed in the presence of God. Over and over again the scriptures say, "But Samuel stayed in the presence of God."

> The boy Samuel ministered before the Lord under Eli. In those days the word of the Lord was rare; there were not many visions...The Lord was with Samuel as he grew up, and he let none of his words fall to the ground. And all Israel from Dan to Beersheba recognized that Samuel was attested as a prophet of the Lord. The Lord continued to appear at Shiloh, and there he revealed himself to Samuel through his word.
> 1 Samuel 3:1,19

▶ **Exercise:**

Read 1 Samuel 3:1,19-21, 7:1-17, and 12:12-25. What did the people think about Samuel? ______________________________

____

____

What made him distinct from everyone else? ______________________

____

____

During that time, the word of God was scarce and there were not many visions. As soon as Samuel began drawing His presence, the word of God began to come regularly. God revealed Himself to Samuel, and all Israel recognized that he was a prophet. There was no one else like Samuel; when he spoke, the people knew that he was speaking the Lord's words. They knew he was a man of God. When Samuel told the Israelites to rid themselves of idols, they obeyed and watched as the Lord subdued their enemies, as he had promised. Samuel judged Israel all of his life, pointing the people to the Lord and away from the ways of the world around them.

Because Samuel was set apart to God, he was a vessel through which God could do his work. God was able to use Samuel to impact not only the spiritual lives of the people and the land, but also the kings and governments of his time.

A Set Apart Vessel

Samuel was not the only vessel that God used in such a powerful way. Many others are mentioned in the Bible, such as Jeremiah, John the Baptist, and Paul, to name a few. All these were set apart unto God; He drew them away and stripped them of the things of the world. He taught them who He is and how to walk with Him; He would then send them back into their environment to work through them with His power and bring impact and change.

Moses is a good example of a vessel set apart unto God. Moses operated under the Egyptian system and mindset. When he tried to bring deliverance the first time, he did it the Egyptian way; he went with sword in hand and killed an Egyptian.

Moses was called to be the deliverer of the Hebrews, but he tried to do it the only way he knew how; he would have never brought deliverance that way. While Moses was in the desert, separated from the culture and ways of his era, God began to change the very man that he was. He changed the way that Moses looked at things and broke him free of the Egyptian mindset and ways. God began to build into Moses deeper humility, dependency, and faith, so that when He sent him back to Egypt, the entire Egyptian system began to crack under the vessel that God had set apart for himself. The whole system of Egypt was shaken by one vessel of God!

The whole system of Egypt was shaken by one vessel of God!

Daniel did not defile himself with the things of Babylon. He was in the land, but was set apart unto God. The kings and people of the time constantly witnessed God at work in Daniel's life and knew that there was no God like the God of Daniel. Through Daniel's life, God changed the mindsets of many kings and began to prepare for the prophecy of Jeremiah to be fulfilled, to make the way for the people of Israel to return to their homeland.

You see this over and over again. A vessel fully surrendered to God can draw the presence of God and be used by Him to change a whole community or nation. This is the way of God.

Being set apart to God is not an option. We must give ourselves unto Him.

Many times we wonder why we can't see the breakthrough, why we can't seem to see transformation and revival come. We need to allow God to set us apart unto Himself. We don't realize how much of the thinking, ways, concepts, and precepts of our land still affect and cover us.

The Presence of the Lord Brings Change

When people abide in the presence of the Lord, seeking Him and crying out for Him, their lives begin to change. They come away from their wicked ways and align themselves with the word of God. Revelation becomes sharper, deeper, and clearer; they begin to see the kingdom of God as it really should be and to move away from the world into the ways of the Lord. They are becoming surrendered to God. When they do that, when they begin to give themselves to this lifestyle of surrender, God begins to create an atmosphere in which He can dwell. The anointing of the presence of God also abides with them, so that when they walk out into the street, they are not just walking by themselves, they are carrying the anointing and presence of God. And it is the presence of the Lord that really makes a difference. When these individuals who are being set apart come together, the Presence thickens, and when they worship, pray, and begin to reach out to society as one, it is as if they could release a wave of power that could have a great impact.

Action Point: Allowing God to Set Us Apart Unto Himself

An important aspect to a life of being set apart to God is that it is not something we do in the past; it is something we continue to do the rest of our lives. We allow God to continually have control of our lives and lead us into abandonment to Him. It is not something that will be completed; it is a lifestyle, an ongoing process.

The Two Components of the Set Apart Life. There are two key components of a set apart life. One is surrender; letting go of our lives, letting go of control, letting go of trying to run and manage things ourselves, learning to become dependant, to become abandoned to Him. We don't try to figure things out, solve or fix anything in our own power or strength. We allow God to plow our hearts; to expose and take out all the self-reliance, the human effort, the things that drive us, even the things in our culture that teach us to turn to ourselves. He begins to draw us out of ourselves and to bring us to a place where we are surrendered, yielded, and dependent on Him.

Two Components of the Set Apart Life:

1. Letting go of our lives — surrender
2. Praying into a real place of trust and faith in God

If we do not allow God to bring that surrender, we find that we will turn to whatever our culture turns to for wisdom, strength, power,

Covenantal position is something that we must fight for; we must continually give ourselves to uphold and strengthen it. It is a direct link between us and God, and we must continually deepen that communion.

comfort, etc. We also find that if we do not allow that kind of depth of brokenness, do now allow God to keep taking it deeper, there will always be some form of stubbornness, rebellion, hesitation, procrastination, or resistance in us. We will always find that we can only go so far with God, that there are places within us that will cause us to pull back. When God says, "Come with me," we'll say, "Why? What about this? How about that?" Our lives will not be fully given over to Him.

The second component to a set apart life is trust. If we let go of our lives but don't fully trust God, we will always be scared, nervous, anxious, or worried. To get to a deep level of trust, we must begin to pray and believe that God is who He says He is. He will build our faith, but we must stand and not retreat or run back into our self-protection, self-effort, or own ways. We have to learn to trust Him more deeply.

Trust is a real place that we continually pray into. God will begin to lead us further and further away from our own ways and our culture's ways; in the midst of that, we will begin to see areas where we really need to pray and come to trust God. We are used to holding onto our own comforts, our own strength, and now God is drawing us out and saying, "Trust me." It will require continual prayer to stay in a place of trust as God stretches and grows us. He will call us to walk out in faith and to rely on Him in ways that we never have before. In doing that, He will be building faith in us and we will be going deeper into the fullness of our covenantal position.

As you walk out this set apart life, you will find that praying into surrender and trust is something that you have to do on a regular basis. You also must continually pray into covenantal position. In fact, if you don't, you will lose some of that trust and abandonment, and will begin to feel the pulls of the world system starting to grip you and pull you back.

Time for Reflection:

What is the most meaningful statement or scripture you read today? ______________________________

What does God want you to do in response to this? ______________________________

As you pray your prayer target for this day/week, what are you feeling the Holy Spirit is saying or calling you to and what is the warfare coming against you? ______________________________

Prayer Time:

Pray into coming to the place of realizing that there is no way we can see this work done if we stand in our human abilities, human strengths, or human thinking. God must begin to separate us from that and to show us how to stand more deeply in Him. Begin to surrender the whole of your life and whatever aspects God brings to light. Continue praying until there is a releasing. Fears and anxieties will begin to arise as you look at letting go of your life fully to God; pray into trusting God with those things and anything else that the Holy Spirit shows you.

Lesson 3.
Regional Lifestyle Change — Raising Up a Holy Priesthood in My Area

Many of you are familiar with the testimony of breakthrough in the nation of Uganda. Before they began to institute prayer altars, the Lord said to them, "Unless you start instituting a network of united prayer all over the nation of Uganda, you cannot overcome the evil principality ruling over your nation. Unless you get a vision that goes beyond your ministry and denominational boundaries and see the bigger picture of My purposes for Uganda, you will never overcome the dark forces, nor begin to establish My Kingdom in Uganda." He continued, "I have so many people in so many denominations, even in places you cannot imagine. Call those who are near and those who are far away to join together. No single ministry, church, or denomination, no matter how big, will ever be able to do the work of bringing My Kingdom single-handedly into any nation; it must be the work of the whole Body of Christ."

Testimony From Uganda

In the late 1990's, Uganda was infamous for difficult situations. Between 1962 and 1986, Uganda had 10 Presidents, bloodshed after bloodshed, war after war, and then finally the AIDS epidemic. The World Health Organization declared the nation worst hit by the AIDS virus; HIV and AIDS prevalence levels were at 36%. The report said that by the year 2000, 30% of the entire population would be wiped out by AIDS, 30% would be infected by the virus, and the rest would be very old people and very young children, among whom there would be AIDS babies.

After receiving the report about AIDS, a government official called a meeting of pastors and told them, "The government has got no solution. The medical world has got no answer. The international community has got no hope. Only God can help us in this." Speaking on behalf of the President, he made an appeal: would the pastors mobilize the nation to pray?

It looked like an uphill task. The first response was hopelessness. What did we do to God? We had one crisis after another. But a young pastor rose up and encouraged the others: "Let's not rise up against the name of the Lord. He has been our help before and He will be our help again. What we need is to humble ourselves, come before Him, and cry out desperately for help."

We cannot bring transformation to our communities, cities, or nations alone. God works with the Body, not just with one single part of the Body. When people come together from different ministries and churches, we gain a new level of legal authority. From there we can contend with the kingdom of darkness.

We cannot bring transformation to our communities, cities, or nations alone. God works with the Body, not just with one single part of the Body.

Nothing Is Impossible for God

This is not an impossible undertaking. It doesn't mean that we have to go find the most renowned speakers or the biggest stadium; it starts at the grass roots. It starts with each one of us being willing to say, "I'm going to establish an altar of prayer, to begin to redeem the land, to pierce through the darkness and draw the presence of God in my heart and in my home." We then start to share with others and encourage them to do the same.

We commit to daily saturating in the Word and hallowing the name of the Lord. We begin to draw deeper and deeper into Christ. And as we start to see God moving in our own homes, the level of our faith is increased and we begin to know without doubt that God can move in our community or city. Then, as we gather with others doing the same thing, we fight for

Testimony From Uganda, Cont'd

As we were crying out and asking God for direction, He said, "Take your eyes off the problems of the land and begin to seek My purposes. As you steer the nation toward My purposes, I will see you through your problems and bring glory to My name. What I will do in Uganda will become a story to be told all over the world." When we began to seek how to pursue His purposes, He said, "The first thing to do is fill the land with altars of prayer."

He told us to set the nation ablaze with prayer by establishing family prayer altars, making every church a house of prayer, and establishing corporate prayer in communities. He said, "The only way you can break the powers of darkness is to repent from the wicked ways that give the enemy authority over the land. And as you turn to Me, I will do what you cannot do, which is to push them back. They may be too much for you, but once you repent and turn away from them, you give Me legal authority to push them back and to set the land free. I can heal the land."

Beloved, the church took up the campaign. Prayer was ignited nationwide. The body of Christ came together and people began to erect prayer altars all over the land – in their hearts, homes, work places, schools, in villages and bigger communities. The government wanted to fight AIDS with condoms. The church said, "No, we will fight AIDS with biblical principles." There was a confrontation from the start, but in the end the government put resources at the hands of the church. The campaign went on and today Uganda is being held up as a model. AIDS has come down from 36% to 6%. To God be the glory.

each other and for God's purposes, heart, and kingdom like we have never fought before.

If we do this individually, we will not be able to impact our land. In fact, we would begin to be drawn back because we will be in an environment that is deteriorating spiritually and we will be trying to hold ourselves up. We need to begin to infect the environment of our territory. To do that, we must begin to build prayer altars, strong prayer altars that have an effect in the spiritual realm. We need to see an army rise up to help spread the level of prayer throughout a territory, beginning to see people awakened and crying out to God for breakthrough. We also need to have a witness to compel others. We need to be establishing prayer altars that are opening things up, pushing back the darkness, and beginning to have an impact on those around us.

Testimony From Uganda

In 1997, the President of Uganda did something miraculous at a repentance and reconciliation conference. After speaking, he got the national flag and handed it over to the intercessors. He said, "I hand over this nation to you intercessors. You are the ones who can bring change. We have tried here and there, but without success. Now Uganda is in your hands."

What prompted the President to do this? A network of prayer that began in individuals and grew into families, small groups, and churches.

What Is an Altar?

From the time of Abraham, altars of prayer were used by God to push back the darkness that covered the land. God promised to give Abraham and his descendants the land of Canaan (Genesis 13:13-17 and 15:7-21), instructing him to move through the length and breadth of the land, and Abraham built an altar to the Lord everywhere he stopped (Genesis 13:17).

The Priesthood

"Priesthood" is the ministry of standing before God to minister at the altar. An effective and holy priesthood draws the presence of God into the land. When the priesthood in the land is doing the right thing, the whole nation will be covered with the presence of God rather than the darkness of the nations (Deuteronomy 28:1-14, Zechariah 3:6-9, 2 Chronicles 31:2-21). In effect, that is what made Israel different from the rest of the nations. God intended for them to be different, commanding them to worship Him only and to never bow down to the idols of the other nations, which would open them up to the ways and culture of darkness and wickedness.

An altar is a place where a priest (or a watchman) stands before the Lord on behalf of the land. The priest seeks to minister to the Lord at the altar and to

- Draw God's presence into the land,
- Stand in the gap and make intercession for the sins of the people,
- Make covenant with God over the land,
- Counter the influence of the unholy priesthood, which seeks to keep the land under the presence of darkness, and
- Establish the principles and laws of the Lord over the land, thus establishing an alternative culture that follows God's ways.

Who Is a Priest?

According to God, priests are primarily the people who are called by the name of the Lord. All Israel was supposed to be a nation of priests (Exodus 19:6). All of Israel's sons were servants of the Lord, with the firstborn son dedicated to God in a special way (Exodus 13:2). This is why God required all men to appear before Him on three different feasts every year (Exodus 23:14-17, Deuteronomy 16:16). In effect, the Levites were supposed to be the ones who led the rest of the priestly nation in ministering to God (Numbers 16:9, Deuteronomy 10:8).

Many things happen at the altar (Genesis 8:20-21, Exodus 29:38-44, 2 Samuel 24:18-25, Deuteronomy 27:1-9, Joel 1:13-14):

- The altar is a place where we can meet with God, which changes us to be more like Him and gives us the power and anointing to change others or to change our land.
- The altar brings God into covenant with the land and with the people.
- The altar is a place of sacrifice and offering.
- At the altar we hear prophetic oracles from God and bring the counsel of God to be established in the land.
- The altar attracts the presence of God, creating the atmosphere for God to work.
- When an altar is serviced continually and powerfully, it pierces the darkness over the land and opens up the heavens.

► **Exercise:**

Read 1 Peter 2:9. Who is called to be a priest? ____________

____

____

According to the scripture, what are priests called to do? __

____

____

Every child of God, whether adult or child, man or woman, is called to be a priest; together we constitute a royal priesthood. We are called to declare the praises of the one who separated from the dark and brought us into the light. Each of us is called to take up our position as a priest of the Lord, standing in the gap for our various nations. We need to teach our families and fellow believers that we are priests—in our homes, schools, and workplaces—and to seek to carry ourselves as priests in our mindsets, in our way of life, and in our commitment to one another and to God.

The Lifestyle of the Priest

The responsibility of the priest is not just about praying and making petition to God. It has the whole concept of instituting an altar, including

- Being the priest at that altar
- Offering your life as a living sacrifice at that altar
- Living as a holy, consecrated people
- Ministering to the Lord and drawing the presence of God
- Bringing your home, community, or nation into covenant with God so that the kingdom of God may come and the will of God be done on earth as it is in heaven

▶ Exercise:

Read the following scriptures involving priests: Ezra 9 and 10, Malachi 2:1-9, Numbers 25:6-13, Leviticus 10:1-3, and 1 Samuel 2:12-36. As you read them, note in the boxes below the Lord's requirements for the priests, and the positive and negative consequences of these requirements being either fulfilled or unfulfilled.

The Requirements for Priests:

Consequences of the requirements being fulfilled:	Consequences of the requirements not being fulfilled:

Set Apart Unto God. The priesthood is what pushes away the darkness, all the influences of worldliness, and the lifestyles of the nations, and allows us to live a lifestyle that glorifies God. This is why the priests were so important to God and had to be set apart and dedicated to Him, not mixed up with the rest of worldly life. The first thing God did with Abraham was to call Him out of His own people, out of His culture, out of His father's household, so that He might be the beginning of a new nation and a new breed of people (Genesis 12:1-4). This has never changed. God determined He was going to have a different people; that is what He has always wanted.

Jesus said, "I was sanctified so that you might be sanctified" (John 17:19). Our duty is to be dedicated and consecrated to Him, obeying the word that sanctifies us (John 17:17). As the priesthood of today walks in these ways, we too will help protect the land and cause God to reign over the nation.

Sacrifice. In the Old Testament, the priests offered animal sacrifices on behalf of the people. In the New Testament, the priest becomes the sacrifice. The Bible says to "give your body as a living sacrifice to God" (Romans 12:1). When we surrender the entirety of our lives to God, we make ourselves a sacrifice to Him, laying our life on the altar, and we attract the fire of God's presence to come upon us.

Prayer and Worship. The Lord told the priests "the fire on the altar should not go out" (Leviticus 6: 12-13). In the days of Moses, the fire on the altar in the tabernacle was continually burning; it was not allowed to go out. Today, the fire signifies a lifestyle of continual prayer, worship, and obedience to God's oracles, which becomes part of the fabric of the daily life of the priest, a lifestyle of unceasing prayer (1 Thessalonians 5:17, Revelation 5:8).

Repentance. The scriptures show that every time Israel strayed from God, it was the priests that the Lord would call back to the altar. And every time the priests left the altar and went to do other things, when God wanted Israel to come back He would call for the repentance of the priests (2 Chronicles 29:3-11, Joel 1:13-14, Joel 2:17, Malachi 2:1-2,7-8). The priesthood is obligated to make atonement for the sins of the people, to repent on their behalf (Leviticus 16, 1 Chronicles 6:49, Hebrews 2:17, Leviticus 12:7,14:19,15). In every nation, in every city, God is looking for a priest who will build up the wall and stand before Him in the gap; who will repair the separation on behalf of the land so that He won't have to destroy it (Ezekiel 22:30-31).

Holy Versus Unholy Priesthood

The Godly priesthood is not the only priesthood. In every land there are two priesthoods: a demonic priesthood and a holy priesthood. The priesthood that services the altar and stands in the gap on behalf of the land will have authority over the land (Hebrews 7:12).

In the story of Elijah (1 Kings 18), before Elijah came, the priests of the Baal were rulers of the land because they sacrificed regularly at their altars and were in constant communion with their demon gods. They had turned the heart of the people to Baal. Even in our day, the satanic priesthood is active and has altars all over the land. As you see mosques, Hindu temples, Buddhist shrines, and witchcraft increasing in the land, you know that it is a physical manifestation of the spiritual activity over your area.

> The priesthood that dominates in an area determines who rules the area.

In these last days, when we are seeing the unholy priesthood dominate and darkness permeate the nations, the need to raise up an army of people who are willing to lay down their lives, to hunger and seek to draw the presence of God, is imperative. The holy priesthood of today, which we are each called into, requires the same kind of dedication and commitment as was necessary for the priest of the Old Testament.

How Do We Build and Maintain an Altar to God Today?

In today's context, how do we establish and build an altar? An altar is a place and time set aside for the purposes of communing with God in worship, intercession, and fellowship. It can be anywhere, at any time, and as often as possible.

The seven essential elements that keep the fire of God burning in our hearts:

- Foundation of the word — a life given to the word of God
- A lifestyle of praise and worship
- Prayer— deep communion and travailing prayer to birth God's purposes
- Prophetic insight
- Subduing the flesh
- Spying on the enemy
- Assigning purpose to time

The Personal Altar. Building an altar starts with a personal commitment to turn our hearts into an altar to God, almost like a sanctuary of His presence, and to commit to do those things that will keep the fire of God burning in our hearts. We must begin with our hearts, even as Abraham did, and raise altars of prayer at specific times on a daily basis to create an open heaven over our lives. As we yield our heart to God, we become a praying, moving altar. Wherever we are we will have fellowship with God, that unceasing prayer bubbling up in our hearts.

The Family Altar. God wants us to fellowship and pray corporately as a family. Many families live together, but inside they are divorced. They don't draw the fellowship and relationship with God into their house and so they are not united. The greatest binding factor in any relationship between two or more parties is God and His word.

Testimony From Uganda

The Lord told us to set the nation ablaze with prayer. He said, "This is how you are going to do it: call every family to establish a family prayer altar. Bring the family to pray together. Bring the family to cry out, not only for their own sake but also to cry for the land, to stand in the gap for the land.

Don't take your children to bed and say a 1-minute prayer, then come to pray to Me as adults; bring your children together with you. Let them cry out together with you.

Let them hear you plead with Me. Let them hear you confess the sins of the land. Let them hear you push back the darkness. Let them learn by modeling it to them."

Your children are the pastors and prophets, leaders and policy makers of tomorrow. If you look back in history, every great civilization's destruction began when the family foundation began to crumble. When there is no effective fervent prayer in the family, you have lost the church of the next generation. It is imperative that we raise up family altars.

The Corporate Altar. The corporate altar grows out of the context of individual and family altars, and encompasses church altars and community altars (where more than one church or fellowship meets together, be it in the workplace, school, or other social setting). It can grow into a city or national altar where people meet at specific times and seasons for the purpose of raising prayer and intercession corporately.

Action Point: Raising the Level of Prayer

One of the things we have learned is that we need to build spiritual momentum if we are going to break through dark powers over territories.

One of the ways that we build spiritual momentum is to begin raising the level of prayer. Each individual, family, church, and community that establishes an altar draws the presence of the Lord and is like a fire that is burning and blazing. When the church begins to rise up, to yield itself to be purified into that holy priesthood, we see the light of these fires penetrating and pushing back the darkness. As we raise the level of prayer and push back the darkness, we will start to see more and more manifestations of the kingdom of God; spiritual blindness will be broken over the nations, woundedness will be addressed so healing can take place, patterns of sin that were acceptable will begin to be rejected and no longer tolerated.

We will start seeing doors opened for unity; doors opened into governments, civic arenas, and other spheres of society; and the Kingdom of God advancing. The priesthood will begin to spread, to arise and begin to connect together so that we can operate as a powerful army in the land.

Conclusion

There is not one denomination or church that can affect a city by itself. No group has the anointing, understanding, gifting, or platform needed to bring long-lasting change; it is going to take the whole body of Christ.

If we are really going to carry this mantle, to draw the presence of God and bring transforming change to our areas, we must come to understand our desperate need for one another. We need to ask God to open our eyes to the urgency of the times in which we live, and the importance of joining with others in our area to raise the level of prayer.

We'll begin to yearn to connect with others in our region. We may lay out a map to begin to get to know the other areas and start to cry out for the east, the west, the north, and the south. We'll ask the Lord to connect us with people and to create a network of prayer all across the region. We will ask God to connect us with people in different faith camps, with different spheres of life, with spiritual leaders, business leaders, educators, government officials, and people from the entertainment industry. We will desire to see change in all arenas of life in the region, and we will begin to yearn to see this spread out all across the region.

We must make more than personal changes in our lifestyle; we must also have a change in mindset. We are no longer individuals doing God's work; we are part of the army of God. We must begin to recruit and join with others in corporate and regional prayer altars all across the area to help push back the darkness and begin to see the Lord bring awakening. It is going to take the people who are called by the name of the Lord coming together as one, with a clear mission and purpose, to bring awakening to our regions.

We have seen this done in many places. It starts with just three or four people who have begun to catch the vision and receive it as a mission. They soon begin to realize that if they are going to see any forward momentum, they have to reach others and begin to join hands with them. This mission could then result in 100s, and in some cases 1,000s, of people coming together to pray. That is when we begin to see breakthroughs.

Time for Reflection:

What is the most meaningful statement or scripture you read today? ______________________________

What does God want you to do in response to this? ______________________________

As you pray your prayer target for this day/week, what are you feeli[ng] the Holy Spirit is saying or calling you to and what is the warfare coming against you? ______________________________

▸ **Prayer Time:**

Begin to humble yourself before the Lord, making a commitment to become a priest in your home, church, workplace, school, and community. Ask Him to show you any area of your heart that will hinder being a priest at the altar who draws the presence of God. Lay everything down before Him that the Holy Spirit shows you, being thankful that He can prepare you to do the work that He is calling you to do. Yield your heart to Him and allow yourself time to rest in His presence. Declare your willingness to be part of the army that He is raising up in these last days.

Lesson 4.

A Mindset Change of Our Mission – Joining the Army of God

We ask that you go through today's lesson with a reverent spirit. Set aside ample time to prayerfully read through the text and then to respond to what the Holy Spirit is stirring in your heart. Please don't feel that you have to respond immediately, but trust that God will lead you into what His heart's desire is for you.

God is raising up an army, and it is us!

Please read the excerpt below from Pastor John Mulinde's booklet, *The Call of the Hour,* © 2005:

> I see a vision of men and women scattered all over the nations—young and old, people of all colors, often isolated and alone—who have a desperation concerning the situation in their lives and in our nation. Their hearts revolt against the tide of the times, against this world system, and deep within them is the growing cry: "Enough is enough!"
>
> They have had enough! They cannot take the status quo any longer. They know that there is nothing within them that can bring about change and they desperately seek God to bring transformation. Their hearts cry out for the truth that only comes from God Himself; they need the God of the Bible. At the risk of deep pain and of losing everything they have lived for, they are turning their backs on the world and giving themselves to whole-heartedly seeking the Lord with all their lives. They are rejecting the compromises and apostasy being taught today and are seeking truth in the age-old writings of the Bible. They are choosing to give themselves to God so His purposes can be fulfilled through their lives.
>
> As they set themselves apart for the Lord, the Spirit of the Lord begins to "draw nigh unto them" (James 4:8). They are still hidden, like Daniel and his friends during their three years of training for the king's service (Daniel 1:3-20), but God is at work in them. He is preparing them for the times ahead. These times will be filled with great trials and temptations. Many will fall and betray their faith. No one will be able to endure unless the Lord himself sustains them. Those who know their God, however, shall be strong and shall work exploits (Daniel 11:32).
>
> I also see small bands of men and women joining themselves

to these hidden leaders. They are mentored and groomed by these forerunners who went before them. This mentoring is not based on academic teaching and training, but on helping one another connect so deeply and intimately to God that He starts to directly teach each individual Himself (Jeremiah 31:33-34). The forerunners share their walk and encourage the others on, like iron sharpening iron, but every person has a direct encounter with God, who teaches and deals with them divinely.

This is an extraordinary company of men and women. They are committed to God and to each other in covenantal, all-for-all love. None is considered greater than the other as they serve each other in humility, yet they all recognize the gifts and callings given to each one divinely, according to God's destiny and purpose for their lives. They willingly make room for one another to take the role God has gifted them for. They celebrate their nothingness and prefer others over themselves in true Christ-likeness.

These bands of men and women are determined to reach out to the lost and the blind, and to breaking the chains of bondage, the veil of deception, and the grip of the world system from off God's people. They immediately come under persecution and misrepresentation from both public authorities and many in the established church. They go about in humility, with fear and trembling, yet they are willing to lay down their lives for the gospel and for the people they are called to serve.

They meet in small groups to pray and seek God. In places such as church buildings, homes, coffee shops, ball fields, and job sites, they come together to encourage and minister to one another. They know that their lives are not their own – that they have been "bought with a price" – that they belong to God (1 Corinthians 6:20).

The Impact

In spite of the trials and difficulties in their lives, the work and ministry of these people who have set themselves apart for God is powerful beyond comparison with anything that has ever been witnessed in the history of the modern church. As they step out, mountains are leveled and valleys are raised up before them (Isaiah 40:3).

Thousands of people across the nation who have unsuccessfully sought the meaning of life in all kinds of ways suddenly realize that there is real meaning to life. The blind are healed, the lame can walk, the imprisoned are set free, the proud are humbled, the greedy abandon their worldly lusts, and the prodigals rush home.

Conventional churches can no longer hold the harvest, so new structures are quickly erected. People begin to join their lives and hearts together and pursue God, no matter what the cost.

This movement keeps growing and sweeping across cities and states, bringing the Kingdom of God into open manifestation. It is not a movement under the control of any one man or organization. Even those who were forerunners are swallowed up in its great surge, and only God is seen to be going ahead of it (Joel 2:11).

I see that as the travailing prayers of these consecrated people penetrate the heavens, the clouds of darkness begin to give way and whole communities become open to the power and influence of the Holy Spirit. The system of the world begins to fall apart. Everything man has ever trusted in starts to give way. While some struggle in their human ways to hold onto their worldly things (becoming more and more wicked in the process), many more find hope and rest in the Lord. Communities begin to change, in all areas and walks of life.

The church is revived and transformed, and families take on a new form of stability and true, Godly love that makes all feel safe and fulfilled. Public servants and political leaders find the meaning of truth, which begins to manifest through their work in public institutions. The nations will be transformed: not by power or by might, but by the Holy Spirit (Zechariah 4:6).

At the same time this is happening, the forces of evil will grow even darker and more aggressive. It will no longer be a cheap, easy experience to be a Christian. People will need to be wholly sold out for Jesus or they won't be able to stand up against the pressure, persecution, and darkness. It will be a battle, but for all those who were prepared by God, it will be a time of great victory.

This movement is not limited to only one area. People who have been called to be set apart are rising up all over the world. There is a movement of hidden people worldwide. Their numbers are growing in Africa, Asia, the Americas, Europe, the Pacific regions, the Middle East, the circumpolar regions of the Arctic, and throughout the islands of the seas. This movement is sweeping across continents and oceans. God himself propels it as He equips His army with a people prepared to weather the challenges of every region throughout the world.

The Call

This vision has already started to come to pass. All across the world, men and women have heard the call of the Lord to be set apart. While some have heard and procrastinated, relying on vain excuses, there are many who have already answered the call and started the walk. They have counted the cost and concluded that it is foolish to keep "chasing after the wind" (Ecclesiastes 2:11). They would rather seek the abiding riches and fulfillment that is found only in the One who has been rejected and misrepresented by His own church in our day. God is already at work in the lives of these people. They are hidden in his safe places, along with those that He is adding to them.

To those who have the Spirit and hunger of God, it is clear what He is doing. The call to be set apart is not to be argued about or struggled against. The choice is not debatable. Human effort has failed to solve man's problems, and the way things are going in the church leaves us with no doubt that if Jesus does not intervene soon, today's church will not be recognizable from the Biblical church of our Lord.

The Lord will not force Himself on His people, nor will He come to us while we are stuck in our ways. He calls us to lay down our lives for His. The glory of God flows where Christ's life flows.

This is the Call of the Hour: Set yourselves apart for the Lord. He will work deeply in your life to prepare you for the times ahead. He will do in you what you cannot do for yourself, and will bring you to the fulfillment of your destiny in the world.

We must come together to do the work of God. We saw in the previous lesson how God called the Ugandans to come together from all denominations, from all faith camps, and all geographical territories and begin to really pray, and as they did, they began to see the powers of darkness being broken. Uganda is not the only story. There are many places all over the globe where this kind of thing is happening. God is working in this hour, but it is not through people who are maintaining the status quo, it is through people who are rising up and responding to God's call.

Personal Commitment — Maintaining a Sense of Urgency. One of the things we are asking is that all of us begin to respond. We looked this week at the responses we need to make and the sense of urgency that we need to fight for. We discussed the need to stand against the spiritual power of slumber; if we don't, it will capture us, as Jesus told us, and it will also keep us from finishing the work we have been given. These are things that need to be impressed on our hearts.

As we consider finishing the work, we realize that to do that we must pray into the mandate constantly. We must be praying into our commission, catching the vision of God's heart, our covenant position, and the instructions and commandments, gifts and promises, and grace and anointing to do the work that God has given us.

Personal Commitment — Being Set Apart Unto God. This builds in us a sense of urgency and gives us a sense of purpose and focus that keeps us from getting caught up in the distractions of our day. We then abandon ourselves to God because we realize that the scope of this work is too big; it is beyond anything we can do. So we surrender ourselves, abandon ourselves, and as God begins to stretch us beyond our own ability, we stay in a place of total surrender and trust in Him.

We must give ourselves to living different lifestyles.

Regional Commitment — Raising Up a Holy Priesthood. In this position of trust, we commit to establishing altars and raising the level of prayer in our homes, churches, communities, and nation. We commit to being part of the royal priesthood, the army that God is raising up in the day and time to push back the darkness and establish His kingdom.

As we do that, people will begin to realize and believe that God can bring change, that He is the only one who can. They will be willing to spend more time in His presence. The past business of saying, "I can't pray" will go away because people will realize that their prayers make a difference. They will want to abide in His presence. They will start spending time before God because of their desperation and they will begin to believe Him to answer their prayers.

We are going to see a people, a holy priesthood, rising up and rising up. If we really begin to walk this out together, it won't be long—less than 1 year perhaps—before we begin to become a witness to our nations.

Mindset Change — Commitment to the Army of God. When the church begins to rise up, we will start to see the darkness being pushed back. We will also start to see more and more of the manifestations of the kingdom of God: spiritual blindness being broken over the nations, woundedness being addressed and healing taking place, patterns of sin and compromises that were acceptable beginning to be rejected and no longer tolerated. We will start seeing doors opened for unity or into the government or civic arena, and the kingdom of God advancing in the different spheres of society. Prayer will begin to spread and connect, and we will begin to join with others in our area and operate as a powerful army in the land. To do this, we will all need a mindset change; we are no longer individuals working for God. We are part of a global army that has a clear mission and focus: to awaken the church and prepare the body of Christ for the day of the Lord's return.

Do you hear the call of the hour? Do you hear the call of what God is doing in our day and time?

Share what God is opening your eyes to see. ______________________

____

____

____

____

____

____

____

Time for Commitment

You cannot go through this study without realizing the urgency and importance for us to awaken as the church. To do this, each of us must realize that we have to join together to see the purposes of God advanced in our day and time; we must give ourselves to living different lifestyles, no longer wasting our time on petty differences or being about our own little worlds, our own little kingdoms. We have got to come together and rally around the purposes of God.

In these last days, God is calling for an army. This global army is already forming. To be part of it takes a commitment and an obligation, discipline that we must all follow. A spirit of abandonment, a willingness to suffer for God's purposes, is also required. This means we must have a willingness to give up things we think are rightfully ours; if it will advance the cause, we give them up, allowing others to step over us. If it advances the cause, we allow it to happen. This is all part of the spirit of God's army.

There is no army that is individualistic. All armies emphasize teamwork and working together with one purpose. When he is enlisted, a soldier knows that he is not only registered to do a specific job, he is actually volunteering to die for the cause; he is also committing to teamwork, to submission, to discipline, to being "one another's keeper"—all the different things that follow the implication of enlisting in the army. Being part of an army is about supporting the whole; it is not about individual talents, anointing, or abilities.

Strategy

God is raising an army and He wants to deploy it globally, strategically, and in specific timeframes. World Trumpet Mission has been called to be part of this army, and by His grace, God has given us His vision and mission for the way forward.

We need to raise up an army that enlists recruits who are willing to lay down their lives, to draw the presence of God, to hunger and seek after God's purposes, and to come together with others to see God's heart desires fulfilled in our day.

The mission of this army is not just to create and maintain a new environment. We have been commissioned to "blow the trumpet" and awaken the church, preparing God's people for the Day of the Lord. We are accomplishing this by raising up a priesthood in the nations that will draw the presence of God and push back the darkness; draw the presence of God to allow us to begin to be transformed into His likeness.

We want to end this study by prayerfully committing ourselves to some very specific things. We will make these commitments in our group. Many times, we can acknowledge that something is true, but not give ourselves fully to it, so we want to make these commitments before other people and before the Lord. We will yield ourselves to God's will, and abandon ourselves to Him, trusting Him to fulfill these commitments through our lives. These commitments include:

1. **Personal:** Commit to allowing God to set you apart unto Himself; you must give yourself in total abandonment to the Lord, beginning to seek Him with all your heart and soul. To help do this, you must commit to

    a. Daily saturating in the word (10 to 15 chapters per day)

    b. Extended times of prayer and drawing deeper into the Lord

    c. Praying into the position of the mandate

2. **Regional:** You must begin to join with others regularly to begin to pray. This is not something we can be individualistic about; we need a corporate sense of calling and purpose, even abandoning ourselves together to seek Him. We must remember, too, that we cannot afford to be offended by one another; we must find a way to come together in unity of heart and purpose.

3. **Prepared to go on mission:** As we begin to join with others, we will asking God to open up the way for the work to expand, for the church to be awakened, for the message to go forth, for prayer groups to be energized, etc. You must commit to being ready and prepared to respond as those doors open.

4. **Continuing ongoing training:** You must commit to be continually equipped so you can be more and more effective as you are called out on mission.

Conclusion

If God has brought you this far in this study, you have joined in heart a company of men and women from nations all over the world who have laid down their lives to see the purposes of God fulfilled in our time. World Trumpet Mission is just one of the different vessels God is using to raise up this army, but it is a vital one. There are not many ministries that God has raised up this way, but this is one of them.

Zones: This movement of God is a global reality; we continually hear testimonies from the different zones about the work that God is doing.

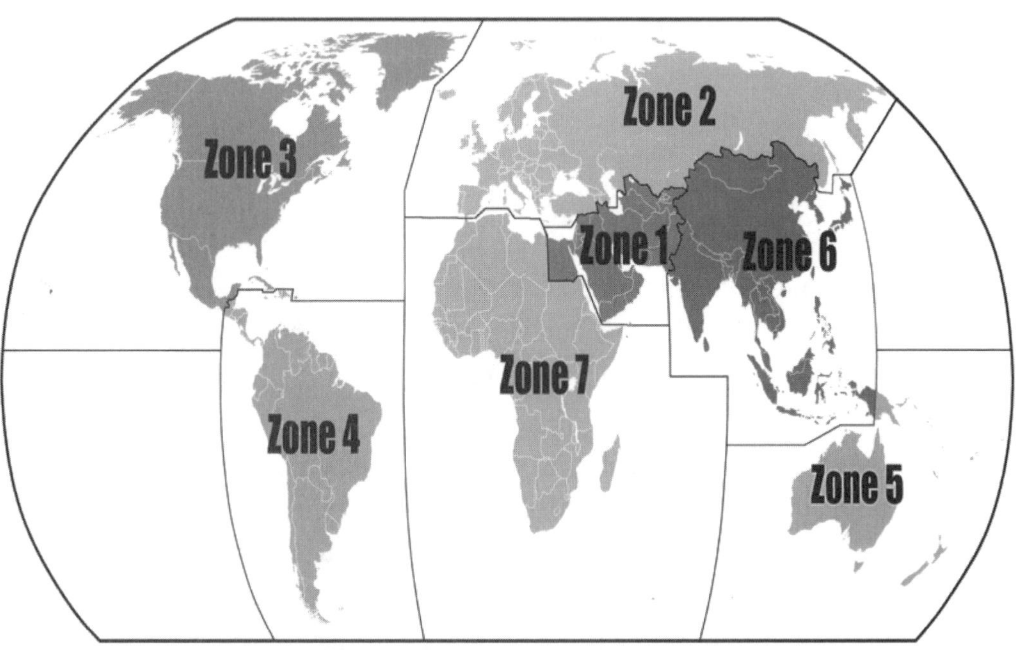

World Trumpet Mission Global Zones

You are joining an army that is all across the nations of the world.

AfriCamp: If possible, we ask recruits to take part in AfriCamp, our annual global meeting that takes place each January. This is a time when the global WTM family comes together for prayer, strengthening, envisioning, and fellowship. Gathering with people from all these different zones has a deep impact and helps envision us for what God is doing in the world today; it helps us get a bigger picture of His mission and heart's desires.

Ongoing training: WTM periodically offers missions training in different parts of the year and in different locations around the globe. Information about such training and/or conferences is provided in our international newsletter, which is distributed bi-monthly. (To sign up for the WTM newsletter, send an email to office@worldtrumpet.com or visit our website at www.worldtrumpet.com.)

Missions enlistment: Each January at AfriCamp, we will announce the mission assignments that WTM will have for the year. This is an opportunity for those who have joined the army and gone through the required training to volunteer for long- or short-term missions into cities or nations that have opened up to the work.

Commitment Card

This is urgent; it is the call of the hour. The time to make the choice is now. You are not here by accident; if you have come this far, the Lord is already speaking to you and stirring your heart. Don't miss out on this opportunity, do not let it pass you by. Israel missed its time of visitation; we cannot let that happen to today's church.

We need to awaken God's people and you need to be part of it. This is not a decision that should be made lightly, but if you turn away you may never get another experience like this again. If you walk away from what God is calling you to, you may even come back to do this workbook again, but you may never again sense the grace and anointing of God that is around you right now.

World Trumpet Mission invites you to join this army. Please fill out the commitment form below, then submit it to your group leader. (You may also mail it to your local WTM office or email it to office@worldtrumpet.com.) This will indicate to us your interest in WTM and its mission, as well as your commitment to joining with us to see God's purposes fulfilled. We will use your information to communicate with you about the work in the nations that God has called us to and how you can be a part of it.

To be a strong member of this army, there are specific commitments that we ask you to make. These will help you in your walk with the Lord and in the battles that you will face. Please prayerfully read each and indicate your answer on the form.

Please fill out the commitment sheet on the following page and submit it to your group leader. Your group leader will be responsible for submitting all commitment forms to the World Trumpet Mission office.

Specific commitments (please fill out and sign the

back of this form):

Personal Consecration:

____ Yes, I will commit to allowing God to set me apart unto Himself. I will give myself in total abandonment to the Lord, beginning to seek Him with all my heart and soul. To help do this, I commit to

Daily saturating in the word (10 to 15 chapters per day)

Extended times of daily prayer and drawing deeper into the Lord

Praying daily into the mandate and my covenantal position

____ No, I am not prepared to make this commitment at this time.

Regional Connection:

____ Yes, I commit to regularly join with others in my area for prayer. I will seek for God to give me a corporate sense of calling and purpose. I will remember that I cannot afford to allow any offense to cause division or disunity, and will love those around me as Christ has loved me. One of my greatest desires will be for others in my area to come together in unity of heart and purpose.

____ No, I am not prepared to make this commitment at this time.

Preparing for Mission:

____ Yes, as I join with others for prayer, I will ask God to open up the way for the work to expand, for the church to be awakened, for the message to go forth, for prayer groups to be energized, etc. I commit to being ready and prepared to respond as those doors open.

____ No, I am not prepared to make this commitment at this time.

Ongoing Training:

____ Yes, I commit to being continually equipped and trained so I can be effective when I am called out on mission.

____ No, I am not prepared to make this commitment at this time.

Please share what you are sensing God is saying to you about your commitment: ________________

____

____

____

____

Print Name: ____

Signed: ______________________________ Date: _______________

Print name: ____________________________ Email: _______________

Address: ______________________________________ (street)

______________________________________ (city, state, postal code)

______________________________________ (postal code)

______________________________________ (telephone)

To be signed by group leader:

Group leader's name (print please): ______________________________

Signed: ______________________________ Date: _______________

Contact information (email; cell phone): ______________________________

Location of Group (city/state, nation): ______________________________

(**Group leader:** Please mail all commitment forms to World Trumpet Mission, PO Box 770447, Orlando, FL 32877, or email the information to office@worldtrumpet.com.)

PO Box 770447
Orlando, FL 32877
(407)846-8300
www.worldtrumpet.com

Leader's Guide

Note to Small Group Leaders:

Thank you for your willingness to lead this small group! Your support, prayers, and encouragement to group members will be one of the most important aspects of this study, and we are grateful that you have undertaken this responsibility. We have written these guidelines with the hopes of helping you and the group receive the greatest impact possible.

We would like to provide ongoing support as you go through this study. To do that, please write to office@worldtrumpet.com to give us your contact information, as well as let us know when your study will be starting and where it will be held. You also may find support on our online blog, which we created especially for you (www.AwakeningTheChurch.blogspot.com).

This workbook lays out a 7-week course of teaching. It is intensive and demanding, but we believe that for those who give themselves to prayerfully and wholeheartedly working through it, there will be significant change and fruit.

In writing this study workbook, the aim and expectation has been that small groups of individuals (ideally, no more than 10 per group) who are working through the book would gather together weekly to discuss and fellowship around the teachings, to support one another in prayer, and to be accountable to one another in walking out the targets and goals for each week.

This is not a normal discipleship study. It is a study that seeks breakthrough in our lives, so it requires that we dig deeper. You will be helping to set that pace, showing people that it can be done. Please include your group members in your daily prayers, and exemplify an attitude of expectancy. This study will have impact and bring change to people's lives.

The Group Leader

As a group leader, your role is to facilitate these weekly gatherings and to help shepherd people along in the study. You will be working through the study along with each group member, so it is not expected that you will have it "all together"; rather, you will humbly lead and enable discussion and prayer in a group setting.

It is strongly suggested that you spend as much time as possible in prayer each day. As one who is helping to guide others through this training, your heart must be set upon the Lord and the message in a deeper way. You will need to press in and pray through the things the Lord reveals to you during the study; you will not be able to help others break through if you haven't been able to do that yourself. In your prayer times, also make it a priority to pray for each member of the group; ask the Lord to break through in their hearts and lives, leading them into position to live their lives fully for Him and His purposes.

Before the first meeting, it is important that you read the preface of this study to get the heart of why it was created and what it's goals and intentions are. You will be setting the pace for the group, so it will be important that you set a good example to the group by completing the lessons each week and coming to the meetings prepared.

Practicalities

The workbook is laid out over 7 weeks, with four lessons per week. This will require a minimum of 8 to 10 hours per week of commitment from each group member, and more for you as the leader.

The first group meeting will be spent in fellowship, getting to know the members of the group, and going over the set-up and expectations of the study. It is important to mention the intensity of the study and the hours that will be required; please share this with the group, have an open discussion to alleviate any fears or concerns, and elicit a commitment from each member of the group to devote as much time as needed to completing each week's lessons. (You may consider creating a commitment sheet that you ask each member to sign and date.) Finally, spend time in prayer, crying out to the Lord for the strength and perseverance that will be needed to complete the study.

At the beginning of each week's teaching, there is a link to an audio file of a recorded message relating to, and reinforcing, the written lessons for that week. These messages are usually between 1 to 1.5 hours long; students are requested to listen to the audio message before beginning the written lessons for that week. Encourage them to let the message sink into their heart and prepare to begin the study the following day.

Each week has weekly and daily "prayer targets," which are meant to serve as help for direction in prayer. These prayer points are one of the main things on which we want to focus because it is only as we are before the Lord in prayer that we will see the breakthroughs begin to come.

Another part of your task as group leader is to help people achieve those targets and begin to see answers to prayer. This will mainly be done as you pray for your group members and stand in your place of seeking to go deeper in Christ in order to lead, but it is likely that you will also need to encourage perseverance and courage in facing struggles and opposition as the study progresses. Much of the message shared in this workbook is to provoke you in spirit so that you will go before the Lord and begin to gain spiritual ground.

There may be times when you find it necessary to minister to people outside of the group time. Some may get stuck or discouraged; it will be very important for you to reach out to them, encourage them, and strengthen them in the Lord. You may need to assign someone to walk with them to ensure that they break through the place where they are stuck.

Finally, during your last meeting, you may consider holding a special time of commitment as well as having a discussion about transitioning your group into a corporate altar of prayer. Both of these activities are crucial to helping your group members continue going forward and deeper with the Lord, and also to help build the momentum needed in your region to begin to see breakthrough and awakening.

Group Meeting Time

Group meetings should last 90 minutes to 2 hours. They should be led by the Holy Spirit and be held in a quiet place where there can be an extended time for corporate worship and prayer.

The group leader should facilitate the discussions by asking pertinent questions. Examples include:

- When you were listening to the audio teaching, what did God speak into your heart?
- Look through the four lessons from this week. What was the most striking thing out of those four lessons that the Holy Spirit revealed to you?
- As you focused on the prayer targets, are you progressing spiritually?

There are a few instances in the workbook where students are instructed to be prepared to discuss certain things in the group time, so be prepared for them to come ready to share their thoughts about these things.

The Commitment to the Army

At the end of the workbook, students will be requested to complete a commitment form. This will be a commitment before God and other people, and will allow your group members to choose to officially say "yes" to what God is calling them to.

For all students wishing to make such a commitment, please collect the commitment forms, sign them as group leader, and mail them to World Trumpet Mission, PO Box 770447, Orlando, FL 32877. You may also email the information to office@worldtrumpet.com.

As group leader, it will be your responsibility to send in the signed commitments. We appreciate your help with this as it is a way for us to know who is interested in our ongoing training and missions programs, as well as who has completed the study and so is therefore prepared for the next stage of training.

Bless you for giving your time to pray for and facilitate your group. May God grant you much grace, strength, and wisdom as you lead, and may you bear much fruit for Him.

APPENDIX 1.

NATURAL DISASTERS:

Major Earthquakes:

- 6th June 2000	7.9 Earthquake hits East Asia – 100 killed
- 13th January 2001	7.6 Earthquake hits El Savador – kills 1,150 and leaves 1 million homeless
- 26th January 2001	7.9 Earthquake hits Gujarat, South Asia. Kills 20,000, injures 167,000; destroys 400,000 homes
- 26th March 2002	6.0 Earthquake in Northern Afghanistan - kills 1,800; over 30,000 homes destroyed
- 21st May 2003	6.7 Earthquake hits Africa – kills 2000
- 25th December 2003	Earthquake in Middle East – kills 28,000
- 26th December 2004	9.0 Earthquake in Chennai, India – kills 212,000
- 7th October 2005	Major earthquake in Pakistan – kills thousands
- 27th May 2006	Earthquake in Java – kills 6,000
- 16th August 2007	Earthquake hits Peru – kills 337
- 30th September 2009	Earthquake hits Indonesia – thousands killed
- 12th May 2008	Earthquake hits Southern China – kills 50,000
- 5th April 2009	Earthquake hits Italy - kills 300
- 30th September 2009	Earthquake hits Indonesia – thousands killed
- 12th January 2010	Earthquake hits Haiti – Over 222,000 killed
- 27th February 2010	8.8 Earthquake hits Chile – 300 killed and 2 million effected
- 13th April 2010	6.9 earthquake in South Asia – hundreds killed

Typhoons:

- 6th September 2002	Typhoon Sinlaku hits East Asia - 1000 evacuated
- 1st December 2006	Typhoon in East Asia - kills 388
- 18th September 2007	Typhoon hits China – millions evacuated
- 5th August 2009	Typhoon Morakot hits Asia – kills 650 and destroys $6.6 billion worth of property

Hurricanes:

- 18th September 2003	Hurricane Isabel – kills 35 and knocks out power to 2 million in US
- 22nd September 2004	Hurricane Jeanne hits Haiti – Over 1050 killed
- 29th August 2005	Hurricane Katrina hits southern US coast – kills 1,636; about $81 billion worth of damage

Cyclones:

- 18th November 2007	Cyclone hits South Asia – kills over 3,000
- 6th May 2008	Cyclone hits South Asia – death toll 22,000

Major Storms:

- 30th November 2004	Storm in Philippines - kills 1,000
- 18th January 2007	Storm hits London, England – 47 killed
- 24th June 2007	Storms in Karachi - kill 228
- 1st June 2010	Storm in Latin America – kills 175

Flooding:

- 2nd May 2003	Floods in Latin America displace 100,000
- 22nd June 2006	Floods in East Asia – kills 200
- 29th June 2007	South Asia floods – 800,000 homes lost
- 10th October 2009	Days of flooding in East Asia causes landslides - kills 186
- 6th April 2010	In Rio, Brazil flooding - kills 200

Miscellaneous

- 14th August 2003	Heat-wave hits France – kills 10,000
- 23rd October 2007	Wildfires hit US – 500,00 evacuated
- 9th February 2009	Brush fires in Australia - kills 181

TRANSPORTATION DISASTERS:

Plane crashes:

- 25th July 2000	Concorde crashes into a Relaise Bleu Hotel in Gonesse, France – 113 killed
- 12th November 2001	American Airlines flight 587 crashes in New York - kills 265 people
- 1st July 2002	Russian jetliner and cargo plane collide in air over southern Germany – at least 71 killed
- 20th August 2008	Plane crashes near Madrid – 153 dead

Miscellaneous

- 26th September 2002	MV Le Joola Ferry sinks off the coast of the Gambia, Africa – kills 1,863
- 1st February 2003	Space Shuttle Columbia explodes over Texas during re-entry into Earth's atmosphere – 7 killed
- 3rd February 2006	Al Salam Boccaccio Ferry sinks in Red Sea – kills 1,040
- 29th December 2006	Ship sinks in storm in East Asia – 600 missing

WAR & TERRORISM

- 12th August 2000 — Russia reports lost contact with Kursk nuclear submarine -118 killed
- 30th September 2000 — Intifada (Palestinian uprising) started by Sharon visit; over 4,000 killed in first 5 years
- 11th September 2001 — Terrorists attack the World Trade Center in New York – Killed 2,967 victims, 19 hijackers; injured >6,000
- 7th October 2001 — Southern Afghanistan: US begins military strike
- 28th January 2002 — Explosions in army munitions dump in Legos, Nigeria explodes - about 600 killed
- 12th October 2002 — Terrorist bombings in Bali, Indonesia – 202 killed and 209 injured
- 12th December 2002 — North Korea reactivates nuclear plants
- 19th March 2003 — U.S. launches war against Iraq
- 16th May 2003 — Terrorist bombings in Casablanca, Morocco – 45 killed and over 100 injured
- 19th August 2003 — Terrorist bus bomb in Jerusalem, Israel - kills 21
- 20th November 2003 — Terrorist Bomb attacks in Europe – kills 30
- 11th March 2004 — Rail blasts in Spain kill 200
- 3rd September 2004 — 350 dead after troops storm school in Russia (Georgia)
- 7th September 2004 — US death toll in Iraq passes 1000
- 17th October 2004 — Report says 70,000 dead in Darfur
- 7th July 2005 — Terrorist bombs in London, England - kills 52
- 22nd July 2005 — Terrorist bomb resort in Cairo, Egypt - 88 killed
- 9th November 2005 — Terrorists bomb 3 hotels in Middle East – kills 57
- 12th July 2006 — Hezbollah kidnapping prompts war in Israel
- 9th October 2006 — North Korea starts nuclear testing
- 18th April 2007 — Bombings in the Middle East – about 200 killed
- 8th August 2008 — Georgia (Europe) under attack by Russian tanks
- 27th December 2008 — Israeli warplanes strike Gaza –kills at least 229 people
- 12th February 2010 — NATO launching major Afghan offensive
- 28th March 2010 — Dozens killed in subway blasts in Europe

ILLNESS & DISEASE:

- 10th September 2001 — Tokyo, Japan confirms first case of mad cow disease
- 13th March 2003 — Hong Kong, China: First official case of SARS
- 27th April 2003 — SARS closes venues in Beijing, China
- 25th November 2003 — 1 in 5 adults in Africa living with HIV/AIDS
- 16th January 2004 — WHO: 4th death linked to bird flu
- 11th February 2006 — Bird flu spreads in Europe through Italy
- 3rd April 2008 — Latin America hit by outbreak of dengue fever – thousands effected
- 18th December 2008 — Zimbabwe: Cholera deaths pass 1,000
- 24th April 2009 — "Swine Flu" (H1N1) in Mexico kills 60
- 11th June 2009 — Global: WHO declares "swine flu" pandemic

ECONOMIC DISASTER:

- 2nd December 2001 — Enron files for bankruptcy after scandel
- 27th September 2004 — Oil rises to $50 per barrel
- 22nd October 2004 — Oil rises to $55 a barrel
- 13th July 2006 — Record oil price of $78.40 per barrel
- 28th February 2007 — Airbus cuts 10,000 jobs in France
- 9th August 2007 — World markets fall after US market decline
- 11th July 2008 — Oil price per barrel reaches $147.02
- 20th March 2009 — IMF: Global economy worst in 60 years
- 17th April 2010 — Volcanic ash from volcano in Iceland knocks out travel in Europe; effects entire world
- 21st April 2010 — Oil rig explodes – kills 11 while oil spill devastates wildlife & coastlands; predicted $1.6 million economic loss

MASSACRES

- 16th April 2007 — Virginia Tech Massacre in Blacksburg, Virginia – 33 killed
- 11th March 2009 — School shooting in Albertville, Germany - kills 15 (plus shooter)
- 5th November 2009 — Shooting at Ft. Hood, TX – 12 killed and 31 wounded